SAFETY SENSE IN THE HOME

BY

HEWARD GRAFFTEY
AND
R.A. McINENLY, Ph.D

SAFETY SENSE IN THE HOME

BY

HEWARD GRAFFTEY
AND
R. A. McINENLY, Ph.D

Safety Sense Enterprises, Inc.
Ottawa, Ontario, Canada

SAFETY SENSE IN THE HOME
by Heward Grafftey and Richard A. McInenly, Ph.D

Copyright ©1990
Registration No. 313289

Cover Design: Karen Rasmussen
Inside Artwork: Karen Rasmussen
Edited by The Editorial Centre
Managing Consultant: Suzanne Sarda, ABMS

 CMHC **SCHL**
Helping to house Canadians

CMHC is pleased to provide assistance in the
production of this publication.

Safety Sense Enterprises, Inc.
P.O. Box 9512, Station T
Ottawa, Ontario   K1G 3V2
(613) 830-9342   FAX: (613) 830-4284

ISBN: 0-921653-06-9

Édition française: SÉCURITÉ EN TÊTE À DOMICILE
ISBN: 0-921653-08-5

DEDICATION

This book is dedicated to the memory of Doctor Arthur Douglass, family doctor for many years in Mr. Grafftey's home town of Knowlton, Québec and to Mrs. Bay Nares, M. Douglas, A. McKim -- all of who tragically lost their lives *In the Home.*

TABLE OF CONTENTS

INTRODUCTION

There are approximately 24,000 fatal accidents each year in and around North American homes. In addition, there are an estimated four million disabling injuries. Disabling injuries are more numerous for home accidents than for any other class of accident.

Identifying the death and injury rates for the many varied products and actions within this home safety book is at best a very difficult task. However, the statistics presented are found primarily in the following accident statistical reports. In some cases where no other data was available, we relied on individual studies performed by hospitals, associations, and private researchers.

- U.S. Consumer Product Safety Commission's
- National Electronic Injury Surveillance System (NEISS)
- Consumer and Corporate Affairs Canada's Canadian Electronic Injury Surveillance System (CEISS)
- National Safety Council Accident Facts
- Canada Safety Council Accident Fatalities
- Art Hazards Information Center, United States

Safety Sense in the Home is a careful study of the reasons accidents occur and what steps we can take to prevent them. Safety Sense also includes hints on how to reduce the danger of death and serious injury, because accidents can happen to us and to our loved ones.

In this book, we have attempted to address each area in and around the home in which accidents occur. A special unit on senior safety has been written because even though older residents represent about 15 percent of the North American population, people over 65 years of age account for nearly 50 percent of all home fatalities. In addition, there are a variety of specialty topics presented that provide safety sense information on a number of home safety issues. These do not pertain to a general home area, such as the bedroom, kitchen, etc. Within each section, the most significant causes of accidents related to the home are reviewed, and a number of actions are suggested to make the home safer.

This book can increase the odds that you will lead a long, safe life. Use it.

THE KITCHEN

The kitchen is the most frequently used room in the house. The activities that go on there create the danger of burns, scalds, falls, cuts, and poisoning. You can aid in the prevention of kitchen accidents, however, by the way you lay out your kitchen. Do a safety check of your kitchen and see how it rates.

Your kitchen will be a safer place if you are able to carry on your activities undistracted by traffic between the back door and other parts of the house or by people dining where you are preparing food. If you live in a house with a back yard, you will want a window over your work area so you will be able to keep your eye on children playing outside.

In the preparation of food, the stove, sink, and refrigerator are closely related. As far as possible, there should be a continuous surface with adequate working space between these elements. Small, unconnected work tops involve additional lifting and carrying of hot saucepans and dishes, increasing the risk of spills, burns, and scalds. The work surface should all be one height.

At least 30 cm (1 ft.) of work space, preferably with a heat-proof surface, should be provided on each side of the stove. This permits hot saucepans to be set down and provides space for handles to project over the side instead of to the front, where children may reach up and pull a saucepan of boiling liquid over themselves.

The stove should be located so that the swing of any door will not bump a saucepan handle projecting from the stove or injure a person standing in front of it. It should be at least 60 cm (2 ft.) from any window to avoid the risk of setting fire to the curtains or blowing out a gas flame. A stove in a corner or in front of a counter where a person has to reach over it to the work surface beyond is particularly dangerous.

Even where local electrical codes do not require it, heavy duty four-pin plugs and receptacles for the stove should be provided to avoid improper connection.

The maximum height of any shelf should not be more than 180 cm (5 ft. 10 in.) above the floor or, if over a counter 170 cm (5 ft. 6 in.). Cupboard doors should not project beyond the front of the counter, to eliminate the danger of bumped heads. If you cannot avoid placing cupboards over the stove, the undersides should be protected so they won't catch fire from the stove.

Many accidents occur when a person must climb onto a chair or other surface to reach high shelves. A full-height pantry with adjustable shelves will eliminate this need.

Adequate lighting should be provided over the sink and stove, so that you aren't working in your shadow. A minimum of 1,300 lux (130 ft. candles) is recommended for all areas of food preparation and cleaning operations, and 500 lux (50 ft. candles) for other tasks.

Gas Appliances

RISK FACTORS
- Poisoning by gases and vapors account for approximately two and one-half percent of home-related deaths.

CONTRIBUTING FACTORS
- burning gas with an excessively high flame
- extinguishing of flame by liquids boiling over
- leaking pipes and faulty pilots
- escaping gas from jets which are not completely closed

COMMENT

When properly used, gas is a safe and valuable servant. Hazardous situations arise when people misuse appliances or use unsafe equipment. Gas users should be aware of these situations and know what to do to prevent them.

Gas ovens, broilers, rotisseries, etc., all have pilot lights and are provided with automatic cut-off in the event of flame failure. If you have any doubts about your equipment, ask your local utility service representative.

Gas hazards may be divided into two main classes: fire and explosions, and carbon monoxide poisoning or asphyxiation resulting from incomplete combustion.

Carbon monoxide is a poisonous gas which can cause illness and death. Symptoms of carbon monoxide poisoning are headaches, tightness across the forehead, fatigue, weakness, dizziness, vomiting, or loss of muscular control.

Pay immediate attention to any odor of unburned gas. If the odor is only slightly detectable, look for extinguished pilots or partially open valves on the range, heater, or other gas appliance. If the source of the gas leak cannot be determined, open the windows to air out the room and call the gas company immediately.

If the odor of the gas is strong and its source is not immediately obvious, open all windows, get everyone out of the building, and call the gas company from a neighbor's house. Do not operate electric switches or doorbells, or light matches, as these could ignite the gas. Use a flashlight if you need light.

- Keep curtains, towels, pot holders, and other flammable materials away from a range. Do not place an appliance closer to the wall or floor than specified in the manufacturer's recommendations, as this may interfere with the proper dissipation of heat.
- Vent automatically-controlled gas appliances to the outside.
- Turn off the gas to the pilot if the flame of a pilot will not remain lit. The pilot may need cleaning, and may then be readjusted to light the burner properly.
- When lighting a gas appliance that does not have an automatic pilot light, apply a lighted match to the burner while turning on the gas. If the flame flashes back and burns inside the burner, turn off the gas for a moment and then relight it. If the flashback continues, this means that the burner needs readjusting and cleaning.
- Open oven doors before lighting the oven burners. This prevents sweating and is a safety precaution in the event of an accumulation of gas.
- Keep the burner parts of a kitchen stove clean. A correctly adjusted flame has a blue inner cone; the presence of a yellow flame indicates that the burner may need servicing.
- Remove the filters of a range exhaust hood regularly to clean them.
- Ensure that your kitchen exhaust system discharges through ducts or directly to the outside -- not into the attic or other unused spaces.
- Tie back long hair and don't wear loose, baggy clothes when working around a gas stove.
- Supervise children around a gas stove.
- Use long matches or a barbecue lighter when igniting the pilots or burner.
- Do not close, with foil or any other substance, natural openings built into the stove by the manufacturer.

Fire

RISK FACTORS
- Every year, nearly 5,500 people die in North America as the result of house fires. Grease fires are the third most frequent type of residential fire.

CONTRIBUTING FACTORS
- spilled oil and fat products
- flammable materials placed on stoves and toasters
- children handling hot appliances, materials, and products
- electrical malfunctions of appliances

COMMENT

Many house fires start in the kitchen; often they are due to careless handling of flammable substances like fat, polish, oil, and spirits. The daily tasks of washing, ironing, and drying clothes, preparing, cooking, and serving food, and the disposal of kitchen waste can carry fire risk because the use of heat is involved. Many cooking fires start when food is left unattended on the stove. The food overheats and begins to burn.

Children playing with matches and the careless use of oil heaters also create fire risk.

SAFETY SENSE

- Never leave food, especially grease, unattended on the stove.
- Never place potholders, recipes, or dish towels on the stove because they may ignite on the hot burners.
- Be particularly careful when using lightweight flammable items, such as paper napkins, light food wrappings, or dish towels. These can be blown onto the burners by a breeze or fan.
- Keep paper towels, cookbooks, flammable decorations, and curtains a safe distance away from the stovetop.

- Don't store food above the stove, where children may try to climb up and reach it.
- Turn handles away from the front of the stove, but not over another burner. This will prevent them from being knocked off and will ensure that children won't grab them.
- Be aware that your coffee maker, blender, toaster oven, and other modern conveniences carry enough electricity to start a fire. Unplug these appliances when not using them and keep all appliances, including large

ones like the refrigerator, clean and in good working order. Inspect cords for damaged insulation. Never cut the third prong off a plug that has one -- it's necessary for grounding.

• Ensure that the room is well ventilated when using cleaning products, liquid adhesives, and paints around a gas stove. These products may give off flammable vapors, which can be ignited and can cause a flash fire.

• Keep your kitchen clean and tidy at all times to avoid fire hazards.

• Keep the burners, oven, and broiler of your stove clean of grease. If your stove has a fan above it, keep that grease-free as well -- a small fire in a pan could ignite it.

• Never pick up a pan of burning grease. Turn off the burner and slide the lid on the pan to extinguish the fire.

• Turn off the heat immediately if a fire starts in the oven. Leave the oven door shut, and wait a few minutes to see if the fire dies out. If it doesn't, make sure you have an appropriate fire extinguisher to put it out.

Microwaves

RISK FACTORS
- Microwave ovens contribute to approximately 15 deaths per year in North America.

CONTRIBUTING FACTORS
- explosion of food products
- burns from overheated foods
- fires caused by overcooking foods

COMMENT

Microwave ovens heat foods fast -- that's why they're among the most popular kitchen appliances today. The growing number of reported injuries, however, should remind us to treat microwaved food as a potential source of personal injury.

SAFETY SENSE

- Handle all containers carefully. Although microwaves won't heat the containers themselves, heat from the cooking food will be transferred to the container.
- Follow manufacturer's instructions carefully. This will prevent overheating, "exploding" foods, and damage to the unit.
- Supervise children using the microwave. Teach them that these appliances are not toys, and that they can burn themselves.
- Test baby foods heated in the microwave. Stir baby foods to distribute the heat.
- Never heat baby bottles in the microwave. The heating is uneven and could scald a baby's mouth.
- Be careful not to splash or spill microwaved foods.

- Be aware that some foods will explode in a microwave oven because the heat generated by the microwaves can produce steam. If the steam is confined, the food may burst under the vapor pressure. An example of this is an egg cooked in the shell.
- Don't overcook food -- this may result in a fire that can damage the oven interior. It's better to undercook food, because you can always add more heat. In case of fire, unplug the oven and keep the door closed.
- Mount ovens on a sturdy, stationary surface like a countertop or a specially-designed microwave oven cart. Be sure you have at least 5 cm (2 in.) of space above, to the sides, and behind the oven for ventilation.
- Use only cleansing materials recom-

mended by the manufacturer. Do not use steel or copper wire or abrasive plastic wool; these can damage the surface of the oven and may eventually damage the door seal.

- For high-current applications at 110 to 120 volts, a three-wire circuit is required. Do not plug a microwave into a two-wire (ungrounded) circuit.
- Make sure that the oven door is in good condition and that the seals are not worn.
- Have a competent technician check your microwave annually.

Knives

RISK FACTORS
- For every 1,000 people in North America, 14 are accidentally injured while using household knives.

CONTRIBUTING FACTORS
- improper use of knives
- poor maintenance of knives
- carelessness when grabbing a falling knife
- carelessness when reaching into a drawer where there are knives
- inattention when cutting with a knife

COMMENT

Knives are used in the kitchen, shop area, outside in the garden, etc. They are used as screwdrivers, door stops, and as scrapers when painting. Unfortunately, knives cause many accidental cuts. When using a knife, it is important to select one that is appropriate for the job.

SAFETY SENSE

- Use a high quality knife with a sharp edge when working in the kitchen. Because dull knives require more pressure, an injury could occur if the blade bounces off the surface of the item being cut.
- Use a large knife whenever possible. People hurt themselves with small knives because they don't watch what they are doing. A large knife encourages you to be more aware of the danger.
- Don't try to grab a knife when it falls accidentally -- you can be badly cut. If a knife falls out of your hand, step backwards quickly, then pick it up.
- When chopping an item that doesn't need to be held on the cutting board, grip the handle of the knife just behind the heel. Place the other hand on top of the blade near the tip of the knife.
- By applying pressure with two or three fingers, you can rock the knife back and forth from heel to tip. In this way, both hands are safely above the cutting edge.
- When you need to hold onto what you're cutting, grip the knife handle carefully with your thumb and first three fingers. The item to be cut should be held securely in the other hand, keeping your fingers away from the cutting area.
- Always pay attention to what you are doing when using a knife.
- Use a wooden cutting board in the kitchen -- its pliable surface won't destroy your knives' edges.
- Store knives in a wooden knife block for safety. Knives stored on magnetic blocks can be knocked off easily.
- Don't place knives loosely into a drawer -- you could cut yourself reaching in to take one out.
- Wash each knife carefully one at a time. Don't throw them into the dishwater along with the other dishes.

Housekeeping and Storage

RISK FACTORS
- Falls account for over 28 percent of all home deaths each year in North America.

CONTRIBUTING FACTORS
- falls attributed to trips and slips on drawers, toys, etc.
- storing hazardous flammable products near heat-generating appliances

COMMENT

Two important measures that will prevent injuries in the kitchen include keeping the walkway areas clear and making sure that everything is put back in its place. You should also organize your storage areas. By making better use of the space in your house or apartment, there will be more room for moving around without tripping or stumbling over objects. By storing things properly, it is less likely that something will fall on you as you put it away or take it out. By storing flammables, caustics, medicines, and other hazardous things according to safety rules, you can protect yourself and your family from cuts, burns, fires, and explosions.

SAFETY SENSE

- Keep at hand the things you use the most. Store infrequently-used items away from the work area.
- Use the lower cupboards and shelves for heavier objects such as pots and pans. One of the problems with most under-the-counter storage space is that the cupboards are deep and awkward to get at. One solution is to fit cupboards with plastic shelves that slide or swing out.
- Use the high shelves for less frequently-used items. Store lightweight things that are easy to handle on these shelves. You might keep your party napkins and plastic containers on a high kitchen shelf. Don't store a heavy ceramic piece, cut glass, or a large mixer where you could strain a muscle reaching it.
- Be properly equipped to reach high places safely. If you are young and agile, use a sturdy step stool. If you are an older person, use a utility ladder with a rail for added support. Older people are subject to drop attack, a condition in which the legs suddenly buckle under. If you have a tendency toward's that condition, be especially careful when working on a ladder.
- Keep things like glue, scissors, tape,

string, and bottle openers in kitchen utility drawers. Sharp objects such as thumbtacks and razor blades should not be kept in these drawers, as they are a threat to unwary fingers. Small plastic boxes with clear tops, like the ones that 35 mm slides come in, make safe containers for pins and needles.

- Check for potentially dangerous products under the sink. If you have small children around, including grandchildren, you should check the labels of the things stored there, and move caustic cleaners, drain openers, and dishwasher detergent out of reach. You can store safe items like large cans of fruit juice, plastic mixing bowls, extra rolls of paper towels, and other things that pose no burn, poison, or cutting hazards. Install child-proof safety latches.

- Ensure that you have ample counter space so that carrying and lifting can be kept to a minimum.

Electrical Fires

RISK FACTORS

• Electrical fires are the second most frequent type of residential fires. They account for close to 20 percent of all residential fires.

CONTRIBUTING FACTORS

• overheating of electrical cords and circuits, etc.
• poor maintenance of electrical appliances

COMMENT

When we think of the hazards of electricity, we usually think of electrocution. But there is another danger -- electrical fires.

To protect against overloads, a circuit should be equipped with a circuit breaker or fuse rated no higher than the circuit's current-carrying capacity -- for instance, a 15-amp fuse in a 15-amp circuit. A fuse or circuit breaker with a higher amp rating will tolerate more current than the circuit can safely carry. This will cause the wires to heat up, especially at weak points such as connections. The heat can ignite flammable material near wiring.

Arcing or overheating can start a fire anywhere along the electrical path -- in the wiring behind the walls, in receptacles or switches, in extension or appliance cords, or in the appliances themselves. Only qualified people should work on wiring or try to repair appliances, but everyone should know enough about electricity to detect problems and to avoid creating them.

SAFETY SENSE

• Consider having new circuits install-ed if you find that overloads happen often. This means that you probably don't have adequate wiring for your needs. On the other hand, if a fuse blows for no apparent reason, and if it happens again as soon as the fuse is replaced or circuit breaker reset, there may be a short circuit.

• Have an electrician check the situation immediately if you smell burning plastic, have receptacles that feel warm, or lights that flicker or get dim. These are signs of serious wiring problems.
• Be especially alert for wiring problems if you have aluminum wiring, which was used in some houses built

between 1965 and 1973. Because aluminum expands and contracts more readily than copper wire, it is more likely to come loose at connection points within switches and receptacles.

- Don't use a switch or outlet that doesn't work properly, until you find out what the problem is and correct it.
- Decide whether you want to use an extension cord inside or outside before you buy it. Does it need a third prong for grounding? Never run it through water.
- Never use an extension cord that has been damaged. Get rid of it immediately.
- Never dangle cords over the edge of a counter, or place them near heat sources such as radiators or toaster ovens. Keep them away from traffic and furniture. Never run cords under rugs, because if the insulation gets damaged, you won't notice. Always pull on the plug, not the cord when unplugging an appliance.
- Keep appliances clean and in good working order.
- Keep motors on refrigerators and other appliances clean. Oil or dirt build-up on electric motors interferes with the motor's operation and may cause overheating.

- Exposed bulbs are especially dangerous in closets -- don't stack things or hang clothes near them.
- When replacing a bulb, check the lamp or fixture for the recommended maximum wattage.
- Keep appliances that may overheat in a place with free airflow. In spite of built-in safeguards, some appliances may overheat if you ignore the manufacturer's instructions on location and use. Don't stack magazines or other combustibles nearby.
- Don't leave appliances that normally shut themselves off, such as clothes dryers, running while you're not at home. They could malfunction and cause a fire.
- Every appliance and extension cord you buy should carry the approval of Underwriters Laboratories, Canadian Standards Association, or another recognized testing facility.
- Don't have electrical receptacles or switches within reach of a person using the sink. Safety outlets with a blade opening protected by a shutter and operable only by a grounded plug will prevent children from pushing small objects into them. Such outlets should be provided in the kitchen, basement, and laundry room.

RISK FACTORS
- There are many things in a kitchen that can cause personal injury, however, most of these are not covered by accident data.

CONTRIBUTING FACTORS
- poorly-maintained appliances
- failure to use pot holders, lids, etc., to prevent injury
- failure to follow manufacturers' recommended safety procedures when using appliances

COMMENT

There are millions of injuries sustained yearly from kitchen appliances, utensils, step stools, cleaning products, etc. Equipment and appliances are frequently taken for granted and used without much thought. This lack of attention can result in minor and serious injuries and, in some cases, death. The following safety sense tips cover some of the hazards in the kitchen.

SAFETY SENSE

- Be wary of enamelware, as it can crack or chip if handled carelessly or if subjected to sudden temperature changes. Flakes of enamel may get into food.
- Do not use utensils, pots, or pans with an interior that is copper or cadmium-plated. Acidic foods can dissolve sufficient quantities of these metals to cause poisoning.
- Beware of using inexpensive tin-plated cookware, which may have exposed sharp corners and raw edges.
- Use pans that are flat-bottomed and well-balanced so they will not tip easily. Lids should be tightfitting.
- Use pots with handles and lids that are easy to grab without touching hot metal.
- Do not use a paper towel to wipe up a stove spill; the towel may touch a hot burner and start a fire.
- Read manufacturers' instructions for safe use of all kitchen appliances.
- Invest in a good can opener -- the safest kind folds the edge of the can under as it revolves around the lid. When using the type that pries open the lid, make sure the can is held down firmly on the table when operating.
- Buy graters that have drilled rather than punched holes. Drilled holes are safer and easier to clean, and are less likely to grate a finger. You may find a grater with a safety guard designed to protect fingers.

- Be careful when using electric slicers, choppers, and grinders. Take special care when cleaning the cutting blades and putting the appliances back together.
- Use a sturdy stepstool and/or ladder in your kitchen. Avoid using chairs or tables to climb on.
- Do not store laundry or cleaning supplies in the same place where food is kept.
- Sweep up broken glass into a dustpan and wrap it in newspaper so that jagged edges will not stick out and cut somebody.
- Try to use small garbage cans to avoid lifting large heavy weights.
- Wipe up food or liquid spills immediately. If you forget, you may slip and fall on it later.
- Be wary of using adaptors when there are too few power points. Do not overload a circuit.
- If you have a mat on the floor in front of the sink, make sure it is in good condition.
- Use a kitchen cooking timer. This reduces the danger of a pot being forgotten on the stove.
- Ensure that sufficient grounded outlets are provided in your kitchen.
- Ensure that you have adequate lighting for all work surfaces.
- Do not keep canned foods that are over a year old, and don't use them if they do not look, sound, or smell right.

LIVING AND DINING AREAS

According to the statistics, unfortunately, home is not the safest place to be; there are hazards lurking behind every door. We are aware of the burning and cutting hazards in the kitchen; the dangers of water, electricity, and medications in the bathroom; the fires, falls, poisonings, and suffocations that can happen in the bedroom. There can be accidents in the living room, family room, or den areas as well, where people are often in a leisurely and relaxed mood. Most of the home accidents in these areas of the house are related to fires, falls, or poisoning.

The living room, family room, or den is usually the setting for parties and special gatherings. When the party is over, two hazards can remain: the threat of fire and the danger of children swallowing a deadly poison -- alcohol.

Before going to bed after a party, empty all glasses and place alcohol bottles out of the reach of children. If you don't do this, your youngsters may get up before you the next morning and discover bottles and unfinished drinks. It doesn't take much alcohol to poison a small child.

If you allow smoking in your home, remember that people are often careless when smoking at parties. Cigarettes can be easily knocked off an ashtray, and people often bump into one another, knocking ashes and burning coals into sofas, easy chairs, and onto rugs.

If there will be smokers at your party, provide plenty of large, deep ashtrays. Remove all wastebaskets from the party area so people will not dump ashtrays into them. After the party, remove the cushions from furniture and feel around for cigarettes and ashes. Gather up all ashtrays and place them in the kitchen sink. Do the same with paper plates and cups.

If you have sliding glass doors in your home, make sure that they are glazed with safety glass. Place a colorful sticker in the center of the glass doors in order to warn people that the doors are closed. This will help to prevent people from walking through the glass and injuring themselves.

Home Furnishings

RISK FACTORS
- Injuries involving living and dining room furniture and fixtures account for approximately 60 percent of all accidents in these rooms.

CONTRIBUTING FACTORS
- bumping into or tripping over furniture
- poor arrangement of furniture
- sharp or protruding edges
- uneven floor levels

COMMENT

The home environment must be adapted to the people who live there. It is important for people to feel natural and comfortable in their homes. The furnishings should, therefore, be arranged so that the easiest and most comfortable method of performing ordinary household tasks will be as safe as possible. This means arranging furnishings and rooms in a way that ensures a safe environment. It is important to take into account the ages, activities, and habits of family members, as these factors make each home different in terms of the type of floor plan and furnishings required.

Poor room arrangements are the cause of many accidents from sprained ankles to fatal falls. A proper house layout should permit effortless movement from room to room.

SAFETY SENSE

- Arrange furniture so that it allows, rather than obscures, circulation. Short and direct traffic paths are the safest. Make sure there is congestion-free passage between the living and dining areas.
- Provide sufficient outlets to serve all normal electrical needs. Avoid overloading circuits and using extra long extension cords. Light switches should be located outside the entrances of each room. Use dif-
fused light rather than direct light, as it causes less glare.
- Use shades that are white or light in color because they give the best reflection of light.
- If possible, ensure that your floor levels are constant. Wall-to-wall carpeting helps to prevent falls.
- Make sure that furniture fits the room. It is important that the size and nature of the furniture suits the people who will use it. Avoid tables that are too

high and chairs that are too long in the seat. If there are elderly people in the home, you should have at least one chair with higher arms, support for the lower spine, and/or an adjustable seating depth.

- Ensure that your furniture is well-constructed, with rounded corners and edges. Improperly designed furniture can inflict serious injury. Pieces should be light in weight so that they can be moved around easily, but not so light that they tip over.
- Avoid using low, heavy couches or other items that are difficult to clean under. It is better not to move or lift heavy furniture, as this can cause physical strain. If possible, use casters which allow the piece to move, then lock in place when not being moved.
- Choose simply-designed pieces of furniture that will result in easier housekeeping and maintenance. Simple furniture also provides greater possibilities for room arrangements.
- Avoid home fires by selecting fabrics carefully. Flame-retardant fabrics do not support combustion and make homes safer.
- If possible, choose doors that swing in and out or have windows so that you can see through them.
- If you have swinging doors, make sure they are spaced or padded at the jamb to prevent pinched fingers.
- Doors should open against walls, and should not interfere with people or other doors.

Stairs

RISK FACTORS
- Approximately 50 percent of the accidents involving home structures (glass doors, windows, fences, walls, etc.) are a result of falling on stairs. It is estimated that 12 percent of all fatal home falls occur on stairs.

CONTRIBUTING FACTORS
- built in hazards (odd-sized stairs)
- hazards created by people (stairs used as storage space for bottles, toys, etc.)
- poor lighting
- running up and down stairs
- failure to use handrailing
- slips caused by poor footing and slippery shoes
- lack of attention

COMMENT

On average, a person climbs stairs 10 to 20 times a day. It's not surprising, then, that quite a few of us take a tumble.

SAFETY SENSE

- Be prepared for an odd-sized stair. Your feet expect each step to be like the next, so any variation in the depth or height of a step can throw you. Try to step a bit higher -- you are less likely to be fooled by differences in step heights.
- Avoid using loose carpeting or rugs on stairs, as they can slip and upset your balance.
- Avoid using carpets with floral or geometric patterns on stairs, as they tend to obscure the edges. You may not notice that last stair until you trip on it.
- Don't use stairs as a temporary storage place for books, soda bottles, boxes of detergent, and other objects. This makes for a hazardous stairway.
- Change a burned-out light bulb in a stairway immediately. A dark stairway is a definite tripping hazard.
- Don't run up and down stairs. Pay attention when climbing stairs and watch where you're going -- don't carry armloads of objects that keep you from seeing your feet.
- Encourage children not to play on stairs, and discourage pets from napping on the stairs. This will minimize the chances of either getting underfoot.
- Be particularly careful on the first or last step. Falls occur there the most. Also, be aware that most falls on

stairs take place when people are descending.

- Avoid climbing stairs while wearing slippery socks or nylons, or pants that are too long.
- Be wary of possible falls on icy outside steps in northern climates. Avoid these falls by keeping stairs in good repair, installing handrails, sweeping off standing water, and keeping them clear of ice and snow.
- Use the handrail -- remember that even the most careful person can trip on the stairs.
- Ensure that step heights on each stairway are uniform.
- Ensure that at least one handrail is provided for each stairway at a comfortable, convenient height.
- Ensure that stairs have adequate daylight or artificial light.
- Ensure that stair treads have non-slip surfaces.

- Ensure that the "rise" of stair steps is not greater than 20 cm (8 in.) and the tread is at least 23 cm (9 in.) deep.
- Changes in elevation should be accomplished by way of ramps or stairs having two or more steps.
- Controls of artificial light should be located at the top and bottom of main stairs and at both ends of long hallways.
- Make sure that doors do not swing out over stair steps.
- Make sure there is adequate head room above stairs.
- Be careful when cleaning windows in stairwells -- especially if a ladder or other climbing device is necessary.
- Balusters (bannister spindles) should be close enough to prevent a small child from placing his/her head between them.
- Discourage your child from climbing or sliding on banisters.

Wood Stoves/Fireplaces

RISK FACTORS
- Approximately 40 percent of the injuries received from home heating, cooling, and ventilating equipment are directly related to fireplaces, wood stoves, and space heaters.

CONTRIBUTING FACTORS
- overloading with wood
- use of flammable fluids to start a fire
- clothing and furniture placed too close to fire
- fire left unattended
- failure to use fire screen

COMMENT

If you are thinking of installing a wood burning stove, keep your family's safety and your homeowner's insurance policy in mind. If your wood stove is not installed properly, it could be a serious fire hazard. Also, your insurance company may not offer to continue coverage of your home if your wood stove and its installation do not meet safety standards.

Wood burning stoves are not required by law to be certified. However, units which are certified have been tested to safety standards and are required to have adequate installation instructions from the manufacturer.

It is therefore in the consumer's interest to purchase a certified unit and to have it properly installed.

If your stove is installed correctly, used with care, and maintained properly, you'll enjoy a safe warm woodburning stove or fireplace for many years.

SAFETY SENSE

- Discuss installation requirements with a reliable retailer/installer.
- Advise your insurance agent and have your homeowner's policy updated before buying the unit.
- Contact your municipality and ask if a building permit is necessary.
  Ask your local or municipal building or fire inspector to check the installation before using it.

- If you have an existing wood stove, check for a certification mark located near the manufacturer's nameplate. If there are any installation deficiencies, have these corrected.
- Maintain your wood stove properly for safe and efficient use.
- Make sure your stove pipes and chimney are in good condition and are checked regularly for creosote

buildup. Shiny creosote deposits look like black paint, and are an indication that your wood stove is not working properly.

- Call a chimney sweep for help if necessary.
- Burn seasoned wood to minimize creosote buildup. Wood that is cut, split, and stacked under cover in the spring will be seasoned and ready to burn in the fall, although a longer storage time is preferable.
- Make sure that the wood stove hinges, doors, latches, gaskets, and operating controls are functioning properly at all times.
- Don't overload the stove with wood. This can cause the wood to smoulder, and produces excessive creosote buildup.
- Keep combustibles away from the stove. Clothing, books, wood, and other flammable items should not be placed near the stove.
- Don't leave your fire unattended for long periods. Ensure that the fire is extinguished before you go to sleep. Ashes should be placed in a metal container on a fire-proof surface, to allow them to burn out safely.
- A dry chemical fire extinguisher should be kept on hand in the event of a chimney fire. Close the damper and air inlet immediately, then call the fire department. Approved smoke detectors are also a good investment.
- Ensure that there is proper clearance between the stove and any combustible surface to the front, back, side, or top.
- Don't connect a wood stove to a fireplace chimney unless the chimney has been properly sealed around the stovepipe. Don't connect more than one stove to a chimney.
- Never start a fire or try to revive one with gasoline or other flammable liquids.
- Make sure your clothing does not catch fire as you put fuel into the stove.
- Do not allow young children to play around a fireplace or stove. Teach them about the importance of fire safety.

Lighting

RISK FACTORS

• There are no national data available on how many accidents occur due to insufficient lighting in the home.

CONTRIBUTING FACTORS

• insufficient lightbulb voltage for work and living areas
• electrical shock and hot lightbulbs

COMMENT

Accurate vision is an important tool for preventing accidents, particularly around steps and stairways, and in areas where machinery or sharp instruments are being used. Proper lighting helps to insure good vision and guards against eyestrain and accidents.

SAFETY SENSE

• Avoid dark colors on large surfaces and counter tops as they absorb light.
• Shield incandescent light bulbs with a diffusing material such as opal or ceramic-enamelled glass or plastic. Fluorescent tubes, which spread light over a wider area, do not need diffuse shielding. Frosted or lightly etched glass or plastic may be used. The deluxe warm white fluorescent tube is suggested for home use.
• Have a minimum of one permanent lighting unit per room which is switch controlled at the entrance, so you never have to enter a dark room.
• Have both general lighting and local lighting at work centers.
• Ensure that your home has ample light at the outside entrances, and throughout the interior. If you have a garage, use two 150-watt PAR 38 floodlamps in reflectors. These can be set under the eaves to provide safe lighting between the garage and house. Make sure that all outdoor lighting has weatherproof cords, plugs, sockets, and connections.
• Provide special lighting for any steps on the way from the street or driveway to your front door. Brackets that provide downlight on steps are preferable, approximately 170 cm (5 1/2 ft.) from ground level, with a minimum of 40 watts each. If you are installing only one doorway lighting fixture, locate it on the lock side of the door.
• Illuminate entrance hall areas with 3 watts per square foot of incandescent

light or 1 watt per square foot of fluorescent lighting.

• Use a shielded fixture with a minimum of 40 watts at the top and bottom of all stairways. Control it by a three-way switch so the light can be turned on and off from both floors.

• Consider using these suggested minimum requirements for major living areas (such as the living room or family room). If the room is 38 to 68.5 m (125 to 225 sq. ft.), use one 150 watt incandescent bulb or four 40 watt bulbs in hanging, recessed, or wall fixtures.

• If you want to use a suspended ceiling fixture over furniture groupings in a room smaller than 68.5 m (225 sq. ft.), the fixture should be a minimum of 43 cm (17 in.) in diameter, with multiple sockets totalling 200 watts. Shield the fixture with an opaque diffuser such as opal or ceramic-enamelled glass or plastic.

• Use table and floor lamps to insure that you have enough light for sewing, reading, and other tasks that require attention to detail. Place the light so that it is not more than 38 cm (15 in.) to the left or right of where you are working. The recommended light for use in a standard floor or table light is a 100/300 watt, three-way bulb, so you can choose the amount of light you need.

• Make sure a light bulb is cool before you try to change it. Don't leave a socket empty -- replace the old bulb immediately.

• Turn off or unplug the light before replacing a bulb. If you forget, you could burn your hand or receive a shock when the bulb goes on.

• Replace bulbs with those that are the same number of watts and the same type.

• Unplug a lamp immediately if a new bulb blows right after being installed. You could have a defective fixture or circuit; have an electrician check it.

• Keep new bulbs in the boxes they came in -- this will protect them from breaking.

Housekeeping

RISK FACTORS
- No national data available. However, dirt and disorder in your home can increase your maintenance costs and the risk of accidents.

CONTRIBUTING FACTORS
- keeping piles of garbage around that can catch on fire
- slipping on wet floors
- tripping over toys, rugs, etc.
- stepping on sharp objects
- not fixing broken appliances

COMMENT

Housekeeping means much more than the daily chores involved in taking care of a home. It includes sweeping floors, washing windows, fixing leaks, and storing things properly. Housekeeping can be defined as any maintenance task that helps to keep a home running smoothly and safely.

It is important to decide who does what around the home, so that injuries can be prevented. Changing a burned-out light bulb, for example, is likely to be done by an adult, whereas tidying up the toys will probably be a child's responsibility.

SAFETY SENSE

- Clean up all spills promptly -- dirty floors are not only unsightly, they also breed dangers to health and safety.
- Make sure that doormats or throw rugs are backed with rubber to prevent falls from sliding rugs.
- Repair immediately missing tiles or holes in rugs.
- Check to see that windows and window frames are in good condition. Cracked windows or frames can break and cause severe cuts when bumped against.
- Remove dishes from the table promptly after meals, to prevent animals or children from pulling or knocking utensils from the table.
- Put dining room chairs, including the baby's highchair, away after meals.
- Prevent falls by tidying up toys, footstools, shoes, etc., throughout the day.
- Keep the hallways clear.
- Arrange furniture so that it does not obstruct traffic.
- Follow manufacturer's instructions when applying wax on floors. Self-polishing waxes should be thoroughly dry before you walk on them.

Dining Hazards

RISK FACTORS
- Three percent of all accidental deaths involve suffocation by food or other objects.

CONTRIBUTING FACTORS
- food that is not cut into chewable pieces
- hot liquid spills
- burns from hot food and appliances
- cuts from utensils
- food poisoning

COMMENT

Many head injuries, falls, burns, and choking accidents occur in the dining room. Children chasing each other may bump their heads on table edges or trip over chairs. Hot liquids can be tipped over and table cloths can be pulled off the table. Try to be aware of these potential dangers.

SAFETY SENSE

- Ensure that young children in high-chairs cannot pull table cloths or hot dishes off the table.
- Keep toothpicks out of the children's reach -- if you are serving them with food make sure they are clearly visible.
- Serve food for babies and toddlers at a cooler temperature than food for adults.
- Prevent choking by cutting baby food into small chewable pieces.
- Keep sharp knives and forks away from young children until they know how to use them safely.
- Never leave a baby alone when feeding -- a propped-up bottle could plug the child's airway.
- Watch your child when feeding her/ him hot dogs -- they are a common source of choking with young children.
- Ensure that your home preserves aren't contaminated. If food appears foamy or discolored, is soft or mushy, if it spurts from jar when opened, or has an odor to it, do not eat the food.
- Simmer home canned meat products in a saucepan for ten minutes before serving them.
- Be especially careful when using electric or gas fondue pots or woks on dining tables. Hot foods or grease can be easily spilled.

Child's Play

RISK FACTORS
- One percent of all fatal falls occur to children between the ages of newborn and 14 .

CONTRIBUTING FACTORS
- falls off furniture
- falls caused by tripping or slipping on floors and rugs
- falls from windows and balconies

COMMENT

Falls are the most common type of accident occurring to children in the living and dining room areas of the home. You can prevent these accidents by discussing falls with them.

Talk to your children about the kinds of games they like to play -- are they inside games or outside games? Let them know that tag and other running games, for instance, can lead to a lot of falls when kids play them inside. Remind them that climbing and jumping games aren't for inside, either. Suggest alternative indoor activities.

Give children a special place to store toys so they don't become tripping hazards. Encourage them to put toys away as soon as they're finished playing with them.

Teach kids to fall safely -- tell them to relax and roll with the fall. They should use their arms to cushion a face-first fall. If they're falling feet-first, they should bend their knees and roll when they land. Practice landing and rolling with your kids on a soft carpet or exercise mat.

Young children should be asked to tell their parents when they've spilled something on the floor. Older children can wipe up spills themselves, so keep a sponge or paper towels where they can be reached.

SAFETY SENSE

- Keep traffic areas free from clutter and electrical cords.
- Equip low windows with safety latches to prevent children from opening them too far. Don't rely on screens to prevent kids from tumbling out open windows.

26

- Make sure that furniture is far enough away from windows so that children can't climb up and fall out.
- Never leave children unsupervised on porches or balconies.
- Ensure that carpets are in good condition and securely fastened down. Throw rugs should have slip-retardant backing or be fastened down with double-faced tape.
- Wipe up spills at once.
- Put ladders away as soon as you're finished using them.
- Don't allow children to play near glass doors and panels. They may fall or be accidentally pushed through them.

SLEEPING AREAS

Over half of the deaths in the home occur as a result of accidents in the sleeping areas. These accidents are primarily caused by falls and fire.

Because falls and fires occur frequently in the bedrooms, it is essential to keep walkways around beds and furniture clear. Design an escape plan from each bedroom and practice it at least twice a year. You can incorporate the bedroom window into this plan. You will need a rope ladder if the distance outside the window is too high to jump safely. Practice sounding the smoke detectors so that all family members will be familiar with the sound.

Waterbeds

RISK FACTORS
- Forty-six percent of all waterbed and waterpillow accidents occur to children under four years of age.

CONTRIBUTING FACTORS
- suffocation caused when the waterbed molds around the face.
- suffocation caused by getting the face caught between the mattress and the guard rail or frame of the bed.

COMMENT

For most people, a waterbed provides a safe and comfortable means of sleeping; however, these beds do pose the risk of flood and electrocution. If the waterbed is properly maintained and used in a normal fashion, none of these things should occur. Caution should be exercised, however, when infant children are placed on a waterbed. There have been cases where infants have died when lying on a waterbed, although there is no scientific evidence to prove that the waterbed directly caused the deaths.

It is rare for a waterbed to become punctured or split at the seams. If this does happen, however, water will seep or spill into the liner, not gush into the air.

SAFETY SENSE

- Place infants on a firm, rather than soft, surface.
- Add a disinfectant regularly to the water in your waterbed to prevent algae from making their home in your bed. Although harmless, the algae are a potential source of odor.
- If you use a heater, place it under the safety liner, not against the mattress. It should not come into contact with water, even if the bed leaks. Manufacturers advise that you turn off the heater when filling and draining the bed. Like any electrical product sold in North America, the heater unit must meet specific safety standards.

Electrical Heating Pads/Blankets

RISK FACTORS

• Although very few accidents (less than 50 injuries) are reported yearly in North America, any electrical product poses a danger if used improperly.

CONTRIBUTING FACTORS

• poorly maintained pads and blankets
• sleeping with pads set at too high a temperature
• electrical shock from broken wires

COMMENT

Heating pads and electric blankets have been used for many years -- pads for therapeutic purposes, blankets for heating capabilities. Both have electrical components and wiring, which means that special care must be taken in their maintenance and use. In addition, heating pads and blankets produce a certain amount of electromagnetic radiation which may cause adverse health effects to some people.

SAFETY SENSE

• Make sure your heating pad is designed for the use you intend -- don't expect to use it continually if it is not made for this.
• If there are "bedwetters" in your home, there can be an electric shock hazard with a warming pad. The electrical element is sealed in a moisture-resistant envelope that can be damaged through pressure or perforation by a sharp object.
• Beware of prolonged exposure to a warming pad or blanket -- it can cause burning. The maximum "safe" temperature varies according to an individual's sensitivity to heat.
• Don't crush or fold warming pads, or pile other objects on them, as this can cause overheating and damage to wiring and thermostats.
• Make sure that you keep instructions on the use and care of warming pads and blankets for future reference.
• Read the manufacturer's instructions thoroughly before using a heating blanket.

• Do not tuck in the wired area of the blanket. Overheating can cause a fire between the mattress and the box spring.
• Don't use pins; they damage wiring.
• Keep the control away from an open window. A cold draft can affect the thermostat making the temperature higher than desired.
• Avoid bunching or folding the blanket when in use -- this can cause overheating.
• Turn the blanket off when not in use.
• Do not dry clean your electric blanket unless instructions indicate to do so. The solvents used may cause the blanket's insulation to deteriorate.
• If you discover a problem in the operation of the blanket, discontinue use and consult the manufacturer or the dealer.
• Check the blanket's cords and connectors periodically. Use and age can damage these parts.
• Use blankets that have been tested for safety by a qualified agency.

Sleepwear

RISK FACTORS
- An estimated 300 deaths annually in North America are caused by sleepwear catching on fire.
- One study shows that eight out of nine victims of sleepwear burns are girls.

CONTRIBUTING FACTORS
- children playing with matches or lighters
- children playing around stoves and heaters
- elderly people warming themselves near fireplaces or heaters
- people falling asleep while smoking

COMMENT

Fires involving sleepwear frequently affect large areas of the body with serious burns. These burns are very painful, cost a great deal in medical treatment, and result in severe emotional stress on the victims and their families. Many of these burn accidents can be prevented. In the case of high-risk groups (the young, elderly, and the disabled), the use of flame-retardant fabrics in sleepwear and bedding greatly reduces the risk of burns.

The flammability of any garment is affected by a number of different factors. Generally, the more tightly-woven, heavier, and smoother the fabric, the better it is at resisting flames. Cotton and cotton blends are the most flammable, while synthetics, including nylon and polyester, ignite less easily.

SAFETY SENSE

- Be especially careful when wearing full flowing garments of sheer material -- chiffon, voile, tulle, or net. Watch fabrics with a long nap, such as brushed rayon and other highly flammable materials.
- Keep your eye on elderly people with poor eyesight, shaky hands, poor balance, and a tendency to fall asleep in chairs while smoking. Like anyone else, elderly people should not smoke in bed.
- Instruct all family members and babysitters on what to do if clothing catches on fire. Never run -- running fans the flame and accelerates burning. Never remain in a standing position -- this allows flame and smoke to rise upward over the face and into the lungs. Always drop into a horizontal position wherever you are and roll over and over to put out the flame. Everyone should be taught this stop-drop-and-roll technique.
- Before you buy, check the labels of sleepwear and bedding to see if they are flame-proofed.
- Always keep matches, lighters, and flammable liquids in a safe place, preferably locked up.
- Be especially wary of sleepwear such as nightgowns -- when on fire, the open bottom creates a chimney effect. The flames are drawn up both inside and outside the garment.
- For safety, buy sleepwear with legs that fit more tightly around the body. Pyjamas and track suits with cuffs allow less oxygen into the openings, thereby decreasing the chimney effect.

Cribs

RISK FACTORS
- Nearly two percent of all home injuries in North America requiring medical attention are the result of accidents involving cribs.

CONTRIBUTING FACTORS
- widely-spaced bars, between which a child's head can get stuck
- decorative knobs that can snag clothing and cause strangulation
- falls out of cribs

COMMENT

Manufacturing standards for crib safety have undergone major changes during the last decade in North America. However, there are many older cribs still in use whose design does not meet current safety standards. After years of use, a crib may lose hardware which causes it to collapse, trapping a child's head between the mattress and the side of the crib. In some jurisdictions, it is a criminal offense to sell a crib that does not meet current government standards.

SAFETY SENSE

- Don't sell or give away an unsafe crib. Dispose of it.
- Be cautious if you are in the market for a crib for a newborn. Don't accept a crib merely because it is offered by well-meaning friends or relatives.
- Make sure that, with the mattress in the lowest position, the distance between the surface of the mattress and the top of the crib sides is at least 66 cm (26 in.).
- Ensure that the maximum distance between side railing bars is 6 cm (2 3/8 in.).
- Make sure that the side of the crib that can be raised and lowered (the drop side) is always secured with two

locking devices. Some cribs have safety stops at the bottom of the tracks on which the drop side moves up and down. If your crib has them, make sure they work.
- Don't buy a crib with decorative knobs on the top of the end panels and colonial style corner posts. A baby's clothes could get caught on these projections, causing strangulation.
- Make sure that the mattress fits the crib perfectly. An undersized mattress will leave a gap at the side or end of the crib where an infant's head could slide down, causing suffocation. There should be no more than a 3.8 cm (1 1/2 in.) gap between

the mattress and the side or end of the crib.

- The recommended thickness for a mattress is no more than 15 cm (6 in.) thick.
- Avoid loose plastic mattress covers or waterproof sheets. They can wrap around a baby's head and cause suffocation.
- Check regularly for missing hardware, broken bars, cracks, and loose parts. Shake, push, and pull the crib to make sure it is securely assembled.
- Look for sharp points or edges, and for holes or cracks where your baby's fingers could get pinched or stuck.
- Always check that the sides are securely locked and that the mattress support is firmly in place.
- When the baby can stand in her/his crib, remove bumper pads and large toys that could be used as steps for climbing out of the crib.
- Never tie or harness a child in a crib. Be sure there are no elastics, scarves, necklaces, or loose cords anywhere in the crib that could wrap around the baby's neck.
- If you are giving away or selling your crib, make sure it's in safe condition and that the original instructions are passed on to the new owner. It is illegal in some jurisdictions to sell a crib that does not meet government regulations and that does not have the original instructions.

Bunk Beds

RISK FACTORS
- Approximately 35,000 injuries involving bunk beds are treated at hospitals in North America each year. Over 100 children died as a result of bunk bed accidents in the 1980's.

CONTRIBUTING FACTORS
- children playing on the bed
- falls from and through the top bunk
- suffocation from getting caught between the mattress and edge boards
- strangulation by catching clothing on a protruding bedpost
- getting trapped between the wall and bed

COMMENT

Bunk beds are a good way of maximizing bedroom space for a growing family. They are also a real novelty for children, providing a fort to defend, a challenge to jump off, and a jungle gym to play on. However, it is important to set safety ground rules at the beginning and reinforce them frequently.

SAFETY SENSE

- Never allow "horseplay" on the top bunk. It can collapse as a result of excessive force on the bed.
- Place beds that have only one railing with the railing against the wall. An accident can occur if a child's body slips between the wall and bed. The child's head can get caught, resulting in strangulation.
- Never allow a child under six years of age to sleep in the top bunk.
- Check bolts and nuts frequently to make sure they are tightly fastened.
- Make sure the mattress fits snugly within the framed portion of the bed.
- Ensure that your children's sleepwear fits snugly so it cannot get caught on a protrusion if the child falls out of bed.

Smoking

RISK FACTORS
- One percent of all North American fire deaths in the home can be attributed to smoking materials.

CONTRIBUTING FACTORS
- falling asleep with a lighted smoking material
- failure to completely put out the smoking material in an ashtray or other safe receptacle

COMMENT

Many fires, particularly those in homes, are started by cigarettes that fall out of ashtrays. Some poorly-designed ashtrays have narrow edges on which burning cigarettes balance precariously. Since the burning end loses weight as it burns, the cigarette will fall toward its heavier end -- and out of the ashtray.

The deadliest cigarette fires are those started when people fall asleep while smoking in bed or in overstuffed furniture. Death can occur from burns or suffocation, which results when gases, such as carbon dioxide and carbon monoxide, are produced by smouldering material. The combination of toxic gases and lack of oxygen causes suffocation.

Burns become the cause of death or injury when smouldering progresses rapidly (such as when a breeze adds more oxygen), and the bed or chair bursts into flames.

Sometimes sleepers awaken because of the heat or smoke and save themselves. However, persons under the influence of alcohol or drugs are less likely to wake up and often die before anyone knows of the fire.

SAFETY SENSE

- If you smoke, use only ashtrays that are properly designed and made of appropriate material. They should be made of a material that will not burn, melt or transmit heat readily, be shaped to prevent the cigarette from rolling or flipping out, and be big enough to hold a half pack of cigarettes. They should not, however, be large enough to be used as waste basket as well.

- Never, under any circumstances, lie in bed and smoke a cigarette. If you decide to smoke, get out of bed and move to an upright sitting location before lighting up.
- Check all ashtrays to make sure cigarettes are dead out before retiring for the evening.
- Keep paper waste away from ashtrays.

Housekeeping

RISK FACTORS
- No North American data available. However, keeping a clean and orderly home does help to prevent accidents.

CONTRIBUTING FACTORS
- failure to keep living and sleeping floor areas clear of objects which can cause a fall
- poor fire prevention practices
- access to poisonous products
- suffocation and choking from failure to keep small play items away from infants

COMMENT

Effective housekeeping can be defined as the cleanliness, neatness, and orderliness of an area in which there is a proper place for everything and everything is returned to its proper place.

SAFETY SENSE

- Teach children good housekeeping practices at an early age. An eighteen-month old is quite capable of picking up her/his toys and putting them away in toy box.
- Keep diaper pails away from infants and toddlers. Not only are they unsanitary, but small children may fall into them and hurt themselves or possibly drown.
- Keep safety pins, hand lotions, medications, etc., away from young children. These items can cause choking, poisoning, and punctures. Try not to keep these things in bedroom drawers that are in reach of a youngster's fingers. If you do, use child-proof latches.
- Keep toys, games, and play materials that are intended for school age children away from infants and toddlers -- they can be very dangerous. You may choose to keep the older children's bedroom door closed, or decide to keep toys that can be swallowed in drawers or on shelves where young children cannot reach them.
- Empty bedroom waste baskets regularly to avoid the possibility of fire.
- Remove throwrugs in homes where seniors live. Falls caused by tripping on these rugs are a major source of injury for this age group.
- Tidy shoes, clothing, and toys up off the bedroom floor before you go to sleep. Serious falls causing broken arms and severe head injuries have occurred because someone tripped over a discarded object on the way to the bathroom at night.

- Be careful not to trip over an animal that sleeps in the bedroom with you.
- If possible, ensure that your home has a fixed fire escape or a rope or chain ladder outside the window of every bedroom.
- Avoid the use of louvre doors in the home because they allow fire smoke to move from room to room.
- Closet doors and doors between rooms can be opened from either side to prevent them being blocked on one side only.
- Don't place ashtrays or heaters where curtains or drapes can blow over them.

BATHROOMS

After the kitchen, the bathroom is potentially the most hazardous room in the house. In the wet, steamy atmosphere, the dangers of slipping, falling, scalding, and electrocution are intensified. Most accidents involving elderly people take place in the bathroom.

If an elderly person uses the bathtub, grab-bars capable of withstanding a force of 136 kg (300 lbs.) should be provided. The bottom of the bathtub or shower stall should have non-slip adhesive strips or a similar finish. The bathtub should not be located under a window, because it is dangerous having to step into the bath to open or clean the window.

Soap holders should be provided for both the tub and shower.

Many accidents are caused by confusion over hot and cold water taps. These should be clearly marked or color-coded. Temperature-regulating valves, while expensive, reduce the danger of scalding.

The washbasin should be securely set in a vanity or supported by legs so that a child climbing or seated on it will not pull it away from the wall.

Poisoning is as great a hazard in the bathroom as in the kitchen. Child-proof catches should be fitted on the medicine cabinet, the drawers and cupboards in a vanity.

Where building codes permit switches or receptacles inside the bathroom, they should be out of reach of a person in the bath.

If infrared radiant heat lamps are used, they should be mounted on or near the ceiling, with a timer switch.

Electrical Appliances

RISK FACTORS

• Approximately three percent of all electrical bathroom injuries can be attributed to razors and grooming devices.

CONTRIBUTING FACTORS

• handling electrical appliances with wet hands
• failing to have a ground fault circuit interrupter installed
• using an electrical appliance in or near water

COMMENT

There are three places in our homes where water and electricity must live side by side: the kitchen, the laundry room, and the bathroom. Slipping on a bar of soap is not the only thing that can happen to you in the bathroom. Many electrical fatalities and other serious injuries occur in the bathroom.

Lamps, heaters, fans, and televisions can be the source of the fatal current in some cases. However, more than half the deaths in bathrooms involve hair dryers.

SAFETY SENSE

• Always unplug appliances immediately after using.
• Do not use any electrical appliance while bathing.
• Do not place or store an appliance where it can fall or be pulled into a tub or sink.
• Do not place an appliance in water or any other liquid.
• Do not reach automatically for an appliance that has fallen into water. Unplug it immediately.
• Do not allow children to use electrical appliances in the bathroom. Hair-dryers and curling irons should be used in the bedroom, away from water.

• Never plug in a bathroom appliance with wet hands, or turn on the water with one hand while holding an appliance that is turned on with the other.
• Clean up all bathroom spills before operating any electrical appliance.
• Install a ground fault circuit interrupter (GFCI) in your bathroom to help protect against electrical shock.
• Ensure that electrical fixtures and switches are not within reach of the tub or shower enclosure.
• For more on electrical safety, refer to page 231 of the Specialty Topics section.

Medications and Poisons

RISK FACTORS
- Poisoning accounts for 17 percent of all home accidents.

CONTRIBUTING FACTORS
- access to medication by children
- failure to follow recommended doses
- failure to understand the poisonous chemical make-up of household substances

COMMENT

The bathroom medicine cabinet is not the best place to store medication because it is easily accessible by children. Also, the moisture and heat in the bathroom could alter the composition of some medicines, making them either less potent or more harmful. Light and air exposure also have negative effects on medicines. It's better to store them in a cool, dry place such as a high, locked cupboard.

SAFETY SENSE

- To prevent accidental ingestion of poisonous substances, store medications, first aid materials, household remedies, and toilet articles in a different place from strong disinfectants, cleaners, and insecticides. Place external and internal medicines on separate shelves. Keep them all out of the reach of children.
- Don't drink out of the bottle if no spoon is handy. Don't take medicine unless you are certain what it is. Recap child-resistant containers securely after each use.
- Clean out your medicine cabinet once a month to get rid of old or expired prescriptions. Throw away prescription medication after its

purpose has been served. Flush liquid medicines down the drain and rinse containers thoroughly before discarding. Dispose of solid medications (pills, capsules, and ointments) by returning them to your drug store pharmacist.
- Discard any medication that has changed color, formed a residue at the bottom of the bottle, or is more than two years old. Get rid of aspirins that are crumbly or give off a vinegar odor, hydrogen peroxide that no longer bubbles vigorously when applied, eyewash or eye drops that are left over from treating any eye disorder (fungus growth may develop in these).
- Protect your children and lock up

drugs, laxatives, astringents, mouth-washes, antiseptics, rubbing alcohol, tinctures, boric acid and sleeping pills. Be careful with shampoo, aftershave and perfume, nail polish and remover, cosmetics, and other beauty preparations. Many products not requiring warning labels can have serious effects if taken in large or even small doses.

- Don't tell children that flavored aspirins are "candy" in order to convince them to take medication -- they may like it and look for more. Although children's aspirin are only one-fourth the strength of regular aspirin, a large dose can be fatal to a child.
- Watch children when visiting or being visited by grandparents who take medication. Many poisonings occur when children go through grandma's purse or medicine cabinet.
- Be wary of medications that may be left on bathroom countertops when you are visiting with a child.
- Be sure to use only one cleaner at a time on toilet bowls, tubs, and sinks unless the label indicates that it's all right to mix specific cleaners. Mixing substances can produce unpleasant-smelling and potentially harmful gases.
- Do not inhale aerosol hair sprays, deodorants, and disinfectants. Aerosols are highly flammable -- do not use around any fire source. Do not dispose of empty aerosol containers into trash cans that will be dumped into incinerators or trash compactors. Aerosols are also very damaging to the environment -- it is best to avoid buying them.

Falls

RISK FACTORS

• Falls remain the number one cause of home injuries in North American with an accidental death rate of five deaths per 100,000 persons.

CONTRIBUTING FACTORS

• slipping on floors
• slipping on the bathtub surface
• tripping on mats and rugs

COMMENT

Falls are the leading cause of serious bathroom accidents. Many falls occur when people are getting in or out of bathtubs. The smooth surfaces of bathtubs, shower stalls, and tile floors, along with soap and water, make slipping very probable.

SAFETY SENSE

• Use rubber mats or safety strips in tubs or shower stalls, and clean them regularly.
• If you are remodelling, consider buying a tub or shower with a slip-resistant bottom.
• Install horizontal grab bars around bathtubs (one in the wall at the front of the tub and one at the side) and in shower stalls. Grab bars should be securely fastened into wall studs or other structural supports, not merely set into plaster, tile, or woodboard. They should be capable of withstanding a static load of 136 kg (300 lbs.). Consider installing bars around the toilet if there are elderly or handicapped people in the home.
• Anchor all towel rings, racks, soap dishes, and shower curtain rods firmly, in case someone grabs them for support.
• Ensure that shower or bathtub enclosures are made of safety glazing material (tempered, wired, laminated glass, or shatter-resistant plastic).
• Always put soap back in the dish when not in use.
• If you are elderly, take special care to prevent a fall. You may not have the strength or agility to save yourself once you begin to slip. As well, your bones may break more easily and heal more slowly.
• If you are elderly and unsteady on your feet, you should use a stool with non-skid feet as a seat while showering or bathing.
• Never leave babies or small children alone in the bathtub or bathroom, as they can drown in small amounts of water. You may decide to keep the bathroom door closed all the time to keep children out.
• Cover floors outside the tub with a bath rug that has a rubberized backing, or another type of floor covering that won't slip.
• Wipe up spilled shampoos, lotions, and water right away -- they can make floors especially slippery. Clothes hung to dry in the bathroom should drip into the tub, not onto the floor.

Hot Water

RISK FACTORS

• Elderly people and children under five years of age suffer more than three times the number of scald injuries than other age groups.

CONTRIBUTING FACTORS

• water heater set at too high a temperature
• young children left unsupervised in the bathroom

COMMENT

Hot water is another bathroom hazard, particularly for young children and the elderly. A child may turn on the hot water just to see it run. An elderly person may use the hot water tap as a support, and inadvertently turn on a scalding shower.

Scalds can cause serious injuries and sometimes death. As little as two second's exposure to 65° C (150° F) water can cause second-degree burns.

SAFETY SENSE

• Prevent scalds by adjusting the thermostat on the water heater so that tap water is no hotter than 49° C (120° F) to 51° C (125° F). Test tap water temperatures with a thermometer after letting the hot tap run for three to five minutes. Lowering the temperature will also save energy and money.
• Be aware that a sudden draw on the cold water supply, such as flushing a toilet, could result in a burst of scalding water while you're showering. Inform family members and guests of this situation or put in a temperature-regulating valve.
• Always check the temperature of bath or shower water before bathing a child or getting in yourself. Keep your hands in the water for several seconds -- what feels fine at first may actually be very hot. Don't test the water with your toes -- if you pull your foot back too quickly, you could lose your balance and fall.
• Install unbreakable faucet and tap handles.

Miscellaneous

RISK FACTORS
- About three percent of all fatal home accidents occur in the bathroom.
- About 25 percent of all drownings occur in the bathtub.

CONTRIBUTING FACTORS
- cuts from broken glass, razor blades
- drowning in bathroom
- head injuries from doors and drawers left ajar

COMMENT

It is not possible to identify all possible causes of bathroom accidents. The following is a list of other, less dangerous, items not yet mentioned. Given the right set of circumstances, however, even these things can cause serious injury.

SAFETY SENSE

- Use plastic or metal drinking glasses, not glass. Avoid using glass shampoo, lotion, and bubble bath containers.
- Dispose of used razor blades in a closed container.
- Move clothes hooks so they are not at eye level.
- Remember to close the medicine cabinet door -- leaving it open can lead to painful and severe head injuries.
- Flush the toilet after every use and close the lid to prevent toddlers from playing in it.
- Don't leave pails with water in them on the floor where a toddler can slip head first into the water.
- Ensure that your bathroom door locks and can be opened from the outside in case of emergency.

LAUNDRY AND BASEMENT AREAS

Laundry and storage areas present another high risk, especially if they share the space with a home workshop, or are located in a basement that is reached by a steep staircase. Too many such areas have only one power outlet, generally for the washing machine. Occupants are tempted to use extra power cords for power tools, television sets, freezers, etc., risking tripping, shock from worn insulation, and overloaded circuits. It is, therefore, recommended that at least one approved outlet be provided on each wall. Heavy-duty four-pin receptacles must be used for dryers.

Meters and fuse panels should be located out of the reach of children. Workshop and laundry areas should be well-lit, and so should basement staircases, which are often especially steep.

All families accumulate some possessions which are used seasonally or infrequently: winter or summer clothing, gardening equipment, tools, etc. These are often stored in odd cartons, creating a fire hazard, and left lying about, creating a tripping hazard. Instead, they should be kept in an out-of-the way area or room on shelves of a reasonable height. Roof or attic space should not be used for storage purposes unless designed that way; these areas must be easily accessible for inspection.

Heating Equipment

RISK FACTORS

- It is estimated that home heating, cooling, and ventilating equipment related injuries contribute to about two percent of hospital emergency room visits.

CONTRIBUTING FACTORS

- poor equipment maintenance
- combustible materials stored near heaters

COMMENTS

The most serious risk posed by furnaces and other home heating equipment is, of course, fire. For this reason, a fire extinguisher is a must in any basement (see Special Topics section, page 205, for more details). It is also important to maintain equipment in good order.

The kind of heating device used in a house can, in itself, be an important factor. For example, floor furnaces should not be used if there are small children in the house. (Floor furnaces are heating units mounted beneath the floor with a single heat register directly above them that is flush with the floor surface. Temperatures of these registers can exceed 149° C (300° F)).

If you are considering purchasing a house, check the construction features of the heating device(s) and surrounding area; older houses especially may be lacking many safety features.

Fuel consumption heating devices, for example, should be vented to the outside (either directly or through a chimney) and have draft hoods or dampers appropriate to the fuel being used. Dampers and draft hoods are necessary to prevent excessive down-drafts that may blow out pilot lights, to control the rate of fuel consumption and heat production, and to provide economy of operation.

Additional or "make-up" air is also needed if fuel-consuming heating equipment is located in spaces that are nearly airtight (approximately 12 psi) are needed to burn one pound of hard coal.

- Install water heating equipment that has a temperature and/or pressure relief valve that can readily be tested. Such a valve should discharge near the floor.
- Check heating equipment regularly for rusted parts and insecure mounting.
- Check vent pipes for rust and sagging; they should be tightly connected to chimneys.
- Keep chimneys in good repair at both top and bottom. Combustible structure parts should not be tight against them.
- Ensure that fuel shut-offs are legibly identified.
- Pre-fab or factory assembled chimneys and vents should bear the label of a nationally recognized testing laboratory (e.g., Underwriters' Laboratories).
- Fuel lines should not extend into areas where they may be easily damaged or ruptured.
- Store liquid fuel only in containers labelled by a nationally recognized testing agency.
- Keep furnace area clear of all combustible materials.
- Especially if heating equipment is in a basement that is often in use, install a ceiling of fire-resistive materials such as fire drywall, fire-resistant acoustic tile, etc.

Laundry Area

RISK FACTORS
- Of all general household appliances (ovens, irons, freezers, etc.), washing machines and dryers account for approximately 13 percent of all injuries treated in North American hospital emergency rooms.

CONTRIBUTING FACTORS
- poor lighting
- lack of space
- flooding

COMMENT

Because laundry areas are generally in frequent use, special attention should be paid to keep them safe. Unfortunately, they are often located in crowded, hard-to-reach alcoves or basements where clutter, stairs, and electrical panels provide extra hazards. Also, because there is often water around laundry appliances, the risk of electrical shock is increased and flooding is a possibility.

SAFETY SENSE

- If possible, avoid having laundry facilities in a basement, which requires many stair trips carrying heavy loads. If you have young children, machines should ideally be placed where you can conveniently reach them without losing sight of youngsters in the kitchen or play area.
- Provide adequate lighting, not only in the laundry area, but on the way there, especially if it is in the basement. There should be light switches at both the top and bottom of stairs. Paint the bottom basement step white so people will not mistake it for floor level.
- Be sure washers and dryers are electrically grounded. A ground fault circuit interrupter (GFCI) is recommended.
- Make all laundry equipment (wringers, washers, dryers, irons, etc.) out of bounds to children. Many machines have mechanical safeguards, but danger still exists. The momentum of a machine during the seconds before it stops after it is shut off is enough to cause a serious injury.
- If your laundry space is near heating equipment, be careful not to hang clothes to dry from or beside furnace pipes, etc. This is a fire hazard.
- Keep laundry area as uncluttered as possible to reduce the risk of tripping. The more table or counter space you provide nearby, the easier this will be. Do not use steps as a temporary storage spot.

Poisons

RISK FACTORS
- About 11 percent of the deaths attributed to poisoning by solids and liquids result from swallowing alcohol: cleaners, polishers, disinfectants, paints, varnishes, gardening chemicals, corrosives, and caustics.
- Poisoning by utility gas and other carbon monoxide accounts for 80 percent of all poisoning by gases and vapors.

CONTRIBUTING FACTORS
- dangerous solids and liquids not properly secured
- furnaces and other gas appliances not regularly maintained
- chimneys not properly maintained

COMMENT

The list of chemicals, cleaners, solvents, insecticides, etc., in the average home is surprisingly long. Sometimes it's difficult to imagine these friendly household aids as dangerous poisons, but they are -- especially in the hands of children. You should be aware of what potential poisons are in your home. Many people have chemicals around that they don't really need; disposing of these -- preferably at a hazardous products depot -- will make one less hazard to worry about.

Poisoning in the home can also result from inhaling hazardous vapors. These most often are associated with poorly ventilated heating equipment.

SAFETY SENSE

- Store bleach, paints, turpentine, pesticides, and other potential poisons out of the reach of children, preferably locked up in a separate metal cabinet.
- Keep all harmful substances in their original containers. Never transfer them to soft drink bottles, cereal boxes, or other packaging associated with food and drink.
- Be sure the lids and caps of chemical containers are on tight. Otherwise, chemicals may leak from fallen containers onto the floor. Open containers also allow chemicals to evaporate into the air, where they can irritate breathing passages.
- If your home has a fuel-consuming heating device, be sure it is properly vented to prevent carbon monoxide poisoning.
- Refer to the Specialty Topics, page 221, for information on poison-proofing your home.

Storage

RISK FACTORS
• Just over one percent of all fires and flames start with the ignition of highly inflammable material.

CONTRIBUTING FACTORS
• fires from oily rags stored near heating sources
• vapors from leaky petroleum and solvent containers
• objects falling from shelves and cabinets

COMMENT

Overcrowded or badly-organized storage space is not only inconvenient, but unsafe. Items stacked carelessly on top of furniture or windowsills can fall. Instead, store things inside cabinets, shelves, or drawers, with heavy items at the bottom.

Stored items should all be properly sealed and protected. You should know which materials are combustible, and which need protection against mildew, corrosion, rust, warping, etc., and store them accordingly. All must be labelled correctly.

People have died by drinking toxic liquids from unlabelled pop bottles. You may know what is in the bottle, but does your family?

Watch that rags, debris, or disorderly collections of parts don't accumulate in your cabinets; they should be storage spaces, not "catchalls."

For permanent storage of tools, many buildings and home workshops have brackets affixed to walls (often over work stations). Sometimes the outline of each tool is painted on the rack where it belongs. The outlines are reminders showing which tools are missing and where they should be replaced. They also save time in locating tools and lessen the possibility that someone will settle for the wrong tool for a job (another frequent cause of accidents).

- Store irregularly shaped objects (e.g., iron) in such a way that they cannot catch on other objects, roll around, or fall.
- Use proper storage techniques even when storing materials temporarily; they may be there longer than planned.
- Use a special cupboard, out of the reach of children and preferably lockable, for hazardous materials.
- Store flammable or combustible materials (including liquids, such as gasoline) in approved containers away from heat and flame. Oily rags can ignite spontaneously, so keep them in airtight and fireproof containers, or wash them out after use.
- Keep large containers, such as heavy cartons, on or near the ground -- but out of the way. This will save your back when lifting the cartons and reduce the chances of dropping them.
- Store powdered materials in airtight containers, not paper bags or cardboard cartons where they may spill or be released into the air by normal air movement.
- Keep liquid containers tightly capped so they won't spill or evaporate.
- Bolt storage cabinets to the wall to prevent them from tipping over and injuring someone.
- Locate closet lights so that combustibles cannot be easily placed against them.

Fire

RISK FACTORS
- Nearly 20 percent of all home deaths in North America result from fire, burns and asphyxiation.

CONTRIBUTING FACTORS
- improperly operating smoke alarms
- poor maintenance of heating and cooling equipment
- incorrect storage of flammable liquids and solids in the home
- poor housekeeping
- careless smoking
- children playing with matches, lighters and fuel

COMMENT

It is absolutely necessary to have a fire extinguisher in both the kitchen area and, if you have one, the basement area. For information on selecting a proper extinguisher, see page 205 in the Specialty Topic section of this book.

SAFETY SENSE

- Install a smoke detector near the electrical panel in your home and, if you have a basement, at the top of the basement stairs.
- Do not store boxes, magazines, old rags or clothes beneath basement stairs. Some organic materials, particularly oils, may ignite spontaneously (without a spark) as they oxidize. Put loose, combustibles in metal containers.
- Store gasoline in safety cans that bear the label of a nationally recognized testing agency, such as Underwriters' Laboratories. If possible, store them outside in a locked shed or unattached garage.
- If you have a clothes dryer, check the lint trap frequently and remove any accumulated lint from other areas. This is a potential fire hazard.
- Have your furnace cleaned and checked by a reputable heating contractor each year, before the cold weather sets in.
- Be sure that heating equipment is in

good condition, securely mounted in place with no severely rusted parts. If possible, install the central heating unit in a separate, well-vented space, enclosed by fire-resistant construction, with a sprinkler head installed above it.
- Clean all combustion air intake openings of dust and dirt.
- If you have a basement that is used often, have ceilings of fire-resistive materials, such as drywall, plaster, or fire-resistant acoustic tile.
- Check furnace air filters at least once a month and replace or clean them when dirty.
- Clean accumulated dust from warm-air registers and air returns; make sure they are not covered by rugs, drapes, or curtains.
- Keep the furnace area clear of combustibles.
- Put garbage in metal barrels with lids to help prevent trash fires.
- Never use an open flame or turn on lights when looking for a gas leak.

General Basement Safety

RISK FACTORS
- Nearly four million disabling injuries occur yearly in North American homes. This works out to about one in every 70 people.

CONTRIBUTING FACTORS
- poor housekeeping practices
- poor preparation for emergency situations
- putting off the correction of hazards

COMMENT

Basements are often full of hazards, largely because they serve so many purposes. Recreation areas, storage space, laundry facilities, workshop, heating equipment, main electrical panel, back entranceway -- any or all of these may be found in the average basement, each associated with its own set of hazards. The very location of the basement makes matters even worse, since it is often reached by a steep set of stairs and is the area most in danger of flooding.

SAFETY SENSE

- Provide a light on the basement stairway with a light switch at both the top and bottom. Also, provide adequate lighting throughout the basement.
- Make certain stairs have handrails that are strong and convenient to grasp.
- Do not use steps for a temporary storage area.
- Paint the bottom basement step white to make it visible and to help prevent falls. Many people mistakenly think the lowest step is floor level.
- Locate electric appliances far enough away from water faucets and other metal construction features (switches, water pipes, gas pipes, etc.) that it is impossible to touch an appliance and a grounded metal object at the same time.
- Never enter a flooded basement if the water is high enough to have reached appliance motors or any electric-

al equipment. Call the electric company and wait for them to shut off the power in the basement. When under water, plugged in electrical equipment and the wiring system can create a fatal shock hazard. The current will travel through water seeking the nearest effective ground, and you may be in its path.
- Tag fuel shut-off and water lines so they can be quickly identified. In an emergency, it is important to find the right one in a hurry.
- Label fuses and circuit breakers to show which outlets and fixtures they protect.
- Keep youngsters out of home workshop areas, and keep these areas tidy and free from oil, grease, chips, sawdust, and scraps.
- Even if you already have a fire extinguisher in your kitchen, keep another one (the multipurpose type ABC) in the basement.

FITNESS AND LEISURE

In recent years, physical exercise and its benefits have become increasingly popular. A variety of services and products has evolved in response to this trend. Fitness centers have sprung up like mushrooms, sports facilities are being used to capacity, and more stores are displaying exercise equipment.

Manufacturers of equipment and promoters of fitness centers often exaggerate the effectiveness of their equipment, exploiting people's desire to be more physically attractive to boost sales. Many people find it difficult to resist the results promised; who wouldn't like to have a young, supple, strong, svelte body with no excess fat?

Remember, therefore, before being swept away too quickly by the fitness fad, that no machine or program performs miracles. Even the best exercise equipment cannot produce dreamed-of curves, eliminate flab, or improve aerobic capacity in a few effortless minutes.

Once you have decided to start an exercise program, you should see a doctor for a check-up and discuss how much exercise to get and whether it is safe to exercise alone in the house. Weigh the benefits and drawbacks of home exercise with those of a health club or other exercise site. Aspects to consider after your doctor's advice, include time and convenience, cost of equipment versus cost of membership, and variety of exercises and activities.

Home exercise has become more practical as cumbersome multipurpose gyms and exercise bicycles have been scaled down, and many kinds of commercial health club equipment is now available in portable home models. All sorts of smaller items are also available, such as ankle, hand and wrist weights, exercise bars, spring-tension chest developers, portable pulley-systems, etc.

Injuries happen when overzealous or misinformed people use their equipment too much, too soon. But even equipment properly used can be a hazard, e.g., a curious child may stick a finger into the fast-turning spokes or unguarded chain of an exercise bike. No matter what type of exercising you do at home, you're less likely to hurt yourself if you warm up before exercising. Here are some tips for a pre-exercise stretching session.

• Set aside enough time to warm up thoroughly. Ten or 15 minutes should do it.

• Never bounce while stretching. Quick, jerky movements tear tendons and ligaments.

• Stretch slowly and gently to the farthest point possible, then hold that position for at least ten seconds. Repeat each stretching exercise several times -- some experts recommend ten repetitions.

• After you work out, spend about five minutes stretching gently to cool down your muscles. This reduces stiffness and aches the next day.

Aerobic Exercise

RISK FACTORS
- Over 30,000 people annually are treated in North America for injuries received while performing dance activities.

CONTRIBUTING FACTORS
- insufficient warm-up of muscles before exercising
- overexertion
- slips and falls

COMMENT

Classes in aerobic workouts or dance are a popular form of exercise; many people find it an effective and enjoyable way to burn calories and tone muscles. But as more and more North Americans jump up and down in the quest for leaner bodies and healthier hearts, many soon find themselves hobbling around with shin splints, strained ligaments, and sore knees.

This doesn't mean, of course, that you should avoid aerobic exercise; it does mean you should avoid overdoing it. The biggest cause of these injuries is the overuse syndrome -- people doing too much, too soon, too often.

SAFETY SENSE

- Before joining an aerobics class, check the instructor's background. Instructors without training in physiology may not understand how physical exercise can contribute to injuries and can inadvertently cause you to have an injury.
- Choose an instructor who really teaches aerobic exercise instead of just performing it. A good instructor monitors her/his students to ensure that the exercises are properly performed.
- Look for an instructor who doesn't try to make everyone conform. If the instructor says, "let's do 20 of these" and you feel like only ten, you should not be forced to overextend yourself.
- Do not start out in aerobics by buying a home workout video. Most of these tapes are not for beginners who need competent instructors to prevent injury-inducing mistakes.
- Listen to your body. Pain is a sign from your body that you are doing too much, or not doing something right. A little fatigue after a workout is normal, but if you're still tired two days later, you know you over did it.
- If you experience any signs of

dizziness, chest pains, nausea or loss of coordination, stop exercising immediately.

- Wear proper footwear to prevent stress on your joints. Shoes should provide cushioning under the ball of the foot, good arch support, and side-to-side support so you don't twist an ankle.
- The best surface to work out on is a raised wooden floor. It absorbs shocks in your joints better than a concrete floor.
- Avoid straight-leg lifts while on your back. Despite what you may have heard, they are not good for strengthening the abdominal muscles. Raising your legs while lying on your back actually gives the hip flexors more of a workout -- meanwhile, it places an enormous strain on the lower back area.
- Beware of toe-touches with your knees locked; they can hyperextend the back and strain it.
- Avoid hurdler's stretch; it places too much pressure on the ligaments within the knee and can lead to injuries.
- Do not bounce while stretching, especially if you are a beginner. You can easily tear muscle fibres.

Artificial Tans

RISK FACTORS
* It is estimated that some 2,000 people a year are treated in North American emergency rooms for injuries received while tanning in booths and under heat lamps.

CONTRIBUTING FACTORS
* overexposure to heating equipment
* malfunctioning equipment
* unprotected eyes

COMMENT

The risks involved in acquiring a "natural" tan from the sun are well-known. They include various forms of skin cancer, including malignant melanoma, which can be fatal; premature skin aging; and serious eye damage, usually to the lens and cornea, although in children the retina may be affected as well. If you are tempted to get an artificial tan, at least follow the safety sense advice below.

SAFETY SENSE

* Do not use a tanning device if you burn easily in normal sunlight.
* Avoid tanning devices if you have a tendency to develop cold sores, because ultraviolet radiation may stimulate their production.
* Don't use a tanning device if you are taking photosensitizing medications. These include many antibiotics and antihistamines (including some over-the-counter drugs), some birth control pills, psoralens (a type of plant-derived chemical), and certain medications used to treat acne, epilepsy, depression, diabetes, high blood pressure, and some endocrine (glandular) disorders.
* Do not overdo exposure time. Start gradually and increase it slowly. Ultraviolet radiation in a tanning booth is so intense that extended exposure can cause serious injury.
* Do not tamper with or modify timing devices in the tanning booth or bed.
* Always wear protective goggles with blue-grey plastic lenses that block ultraviolet light. Simply closing your eyes, using regular sunglasses, or putting cotton balls over your eyes will not protect you.
* Use a lip protector cream that screens ultraviolet light.
* Avoid direct contact with the sunlamp. Tanning booths should have hand-rails so people using them can maintain their balance and stay a proper distance from the lamps.
* Be sure an attendant is always nearby to help in an emergency.
* If you change tanning salons, tell the personnel there about your previous tanning exposure.

Selecting Home Exercise Equipment

RISK FACTORS
* It is estimated that some 20,000 people each year in North America are treated for injuries received while working with home exercise equipment.

CONTRIBUTING FACTORS
* failure to read operating manual
* failure to adhere to safety precautions
* overexertion
* children left unattended around equipment

COMMENT

You may want to consult a professional exercise physiologist or sports medicine doctor before buying your equipment. These experts can give individualized evaluations and offer advice on how to work out on a piece of equipment and which pieces to use to meet your specific needs. The YMCA/YWCA also trains experts who are qualified to evaluate your muscular strength, cardiovascular fitness, flexibility, and lean body weight.

If you buy safe equipment and then use it right, you can ensure that your equipment will build you up -- not break down.

SAFETY SENSE

* Make sure you have room for your home gym. Remember that you'll need good ventilation as you work up a sweat.
* On hard floors, use a thick mat to protect your back.
* Consider what safety features are needed to protect your family. If there are handicapped people or young children in the home, look for built-in safety guards and be prepared to supervise and properly store the equipment at all times.
* Try to determine the strength and safety of a piece of equipment by testing it out in the store whenever possible. How smoothly does it operate? Can you safely and easily change the machine from one exercise function to another? Is it sturdy, or does it shift on the floor or shake when used at maximum resistance or speed?
* Be especially cautious when purchasing an exercise device through the mail, as you can't examine it beforehand. Check the company's return policy in case you are dissatisfied with the equipment.
* Pay attention to what you are getting

for the price of exercise equipment. You may not want to pay for an expensive model that has an ergometer and a sleek design that is nice, but not necessary. On the other hand, a less expensive model may be cheaply made, less sturdy, and more apt to break down.

- Look for heavy tubular steel and strong bolts, rather than thin screws and pins. If the equipment is electrical, it should carry a marker from Underwriters' Laboratories, Canadian Standards Association, or another recognized testing laboratory.
- Check that moving parts, such as chains on exercise bicycles, are guarded. Look for strong steel or coated cables rather than bare nylon or fabric, which may eventually fray.
- Before buying, read the operating manual and ask the salesperson to point out potential hazards. Even well-built equipment can be unsafe if used improperly; always follow the manufacturers' recommendations for safe operation.
- Store rowing machines in an upright position when not in use. Because the seat glides easily back and forth, children may see it as a plaything, and perhaps fall off.
- Watch out for collars on free weights that can loosen up during use, sending the weights crashing to the floor.
- Repair or replace any device that needs maintenance to avoid hazards that come with wear, such as loose bolts, springs and handles. Although your body becomes stronger with use, your exercise equipment will not.

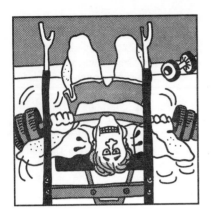

Weight Lifting and Children

RISK FACTORS
• Half of the estimated 44,000 weight lifting injuries treated in North American hospital emergency rooms last year happened to children ten to 19 years old.

CONTRIBUTING FACTORS
• lifting too much weight
• equipment falling on an individual
• lack of supervision

COMMENT

Not so long ago, body builders and Olympic weight lifters were just about the only people doing presses and curls. But today, many teenagers and even young children work out with weights. Although most weight lifting injuries are only minor sprains and strains, many parents are concerned enough to ask questions about the safety and benefits of weight lifting for their sons and daughters.

Physicians see little value for weight lifting in young athletes. Hoisting the maximum amount of weight in a single lift is a goal for Olympic competitors; when a child tries it, the result is frequently an injury.

Even weight training may not be of much value to pre-adolescent boys. Testosterone, the male hormone that enables muscle size to increase, is not present in levels that would increase muscle mass in boys who have not reached puberty. Some physicians are concerned that young children who lift too-heavy weights may suffer injuries to developing bones if they do it often.

Yet most experts feel that, although the benefits will be minimal, no harm will come to a child who works out with light weights under supervision and proper instruction. The best advice for a youngster interested in working out with weights is: Get some help from an experienced trainer, and don't overdo.

SAFETY SENSE

• Be sure youngsters work out only under supervision and instruction. It's often the youngster lifting weights at home without guidance who puts too much weight on a bar and gets hurt.
• Teach youngsters to start with light weights and work up slowly. Even

when they go to a gym for instruction, children tend to be overenthusiastic when they begin working with weights and suffer injuries as a consequence.

• Be sure young lifters who work out at home have spotters to lend a hand if they do lift too much. Weight lifters have died when a barbell turned out to be too much to handle and landed on the lifter's throat and chest.

• Remember that even if at-home lifters are conscientious about safety and keep the weights light, they may not benefit much from workouts if they don't follow programs that exercise all muscles. Working on one set of muscles and ignoring others sets the young athlete up for potential injuries in unexercised areas.

Saunas, Whirlpools and Hot Tubs

RISK FACTORS
• It is estimated that more than 2,000 people in North America are treated at emergency rooms for injuries received while using a sauna or tub. Many of these injuries are related to alcohol consumption.

CONTRIBUTING FACTORS
• alcohol
• overexposure to heat
• overheated water
• malfunctioning equipment
• electrical shock
• fire

COMMENT

Reclining in a hot tub or whirlpool is, for some people, the height of relaxation -- but it is not without hazards. Remember that intense heat, water, and electricity are all involved. The danger increases whenever alcohol and hot water are mixed. Alcohol is a relaxant-depressant: it causes dilation of the capillaries of the skin, which produces reddening and a general feeling of relaxation. And, say the experts, heat produces the same results. Remember this when you are next tempted to soak in your spa or tub with a glass of wine.

SAFETY SENSE

• If you suffer from heart disease, diabetes, or high or low blood pressure, do not enter a spa without prior medical consultation.
• Always check spa water temperature before use. Never allow the temperature of the spa water to exceed 40° C (104° F).
• Never use a spa while under the influence of alcohol, anticoagulants, antihistamines, vasoconstrictors, vasodilators, stimulants, hypnotics, narcotics, or tranquilizers.
• Observe a reasonable time limit; long exposures may result in nausea, dizziness or fainting. If you wish, return for another brief stay after

showering and cooling down.
• Always enter and exit the spa slowly and cautiously.
• Never allow children to use the spa without supervision.
• Ensure that there is a barrier around or a cover over your spa to keep children from playing in it.
• Avoid using the spa alone.
• List emergency numbers by the nearest phone: police, fire and/or rescue unit, physician, ambulance service and hospital.
• Shower before and after a hot tub session, and wear a bathing cap to protect against scalp infections such as ringworms.

- Keep your hot tub clean to prevent the breeding and transmittal of bacteria such as diarrhea, vaginitis, and athlete's foot.
- Make sure all electrical plugs have a ground fault interrupter to protect the user against electrical shocks.
- Use non-skid flooring around the spa equipment to help prevent slips and falls.
- Keep electrical appliances, such as radios, stereos and bar fridges, out of the spa area.
- Use a timer switch on the spa setting to manufacturer's recommended exposure limits. Install it well out of the reach of children.
- Avoid using a hot tub if you are pregnant. A pregnant woman's larger circulatory system can transmit excessive heat to an unborn child.

The Bar

RISK FACTORS
• No North American data available. However, many persons are injured from falling off kitchen and bar stools. Although, not all of these injuries are a result of intoxication.

CONTRIBUTING FACTORS
• intoxication
• loss of balance

COMMENT

Many people do not realize that even if they do their drinking at home, the resulting impairment can lead to injury. The concentration of alcohol in your blood is related to the degree of impairment. The following chart will assist you in estimating this concentration.

1. Count your drinks [one drink equals 43 ml (1½ oz.) of spirits or 85 ml (3 oz.) of wine or 341 ml (12 oz.) of beer].

2. Refer to the chart on the next page. Under the number of drinks and opposite your body weight, find the percent of blood alcohol listed.

3. It takes the body about one hour to eliminate one drink [e.g., 43 ml (11/2 oz.) of spirits], so subtract the percent of alcohol burned up in your body during the time elapsed since your first drink. The resulting number would represent approximately your present blood alcohol concentration. Remember, this is only an estimate. Other factors, such as experience in drinking, amount of food in your stomach, etc., will affect your state of impairment. Remember that .10% equals 100 mg% or .08% equals 80 mg%.

BODY WEIGHT	NUMBER OF DRINKS IN MG %								
	1	2	3	4	5	6	7	8	9
45KG (100 LBS)	43	87	130	174	217	261	304	348	319
56KG (125 LBS)	34	69	103	139	173	209	242	278	312
68KG (150 LBS)	29	58	87	116	145	174	203	232	261
79KG (175 LBS)	25	50	75	100	125	150	175	200	225
90KG (200 LBS)	22	43	65	87	108	130	152	174	195
102KG (225 LBS)	19	39	58	78	97	117	136	156	175
113KG (250 LBS)	17	37	52	70	87	105	122	139	156

Hours since drinking started	1	2	3	4
% of alcohol burned	15mg%	30mg%	45mg%	60mg%

Example: Based on the chart, a 56 kg (125 lb) person who consumes three drinks in one hour has an approximate blood alcohol level of 103 mg%. After a two-hour time lapse, his blood alcohol level is 73 mg% (103-30=73).

THE YARD

A yard, whether it be around a private, multiple, or apartment dwelling, should be a pleasant environment in the open around your home. Care is needed, however, to ensure that the yard area is not only beautiful and enjoyable, but safe.

Paved surfaces should have a rough finish to prevent slipping. The fewer steps, the better -- ramps are safer and can accommodate baby carriages and wheelchairs. If you use cobbles or loose stones as a surface, they should be clearly visible and preferably located at a separate level to avoid twisted ankles.

Prune tree branches that overhang paths or steps. Fallen and slippery leaves could cause a hazard. Also, ensure that hedges, trees, or shrubs do not obscure the view of the street from the driveway, or of a child heading toward the driveway from the lawn or house.

Walkways and driveways should be properly sloped to drains to avoid standing water, which may freeze. If a walkway is bordered by a barrier, such as a wall or raised planter, be sure it is high enough -- 45-60 cm (17-23 in.) -- to be clearly visible. Also, be sure walkways are well lit for personal safety. Lighting standards should be high enough to prevent vandalism, a minimum of 2.5 m (8 ft.). Toughened acrylic plastic or fibreglass globes or shades provide better protection than glass and do not splinter when broken.

Covered or underground parking areas also need adequate lighting to reduce the risk of traffic accidents, crime, and vandalism. A minimum of five foot-candles (50 lux) at ground level is recommended by the Illuminating Engineers Society.

Build vertical-style fences, instead of horizontal-style ones to discourage climbing. Upright components of fences should have rounded ends, and where chain-link fencing is used, care should be taken that there are no protruding pieces of wire. Copings to brick walls should be firmly tied down by metal straps or rods so that they cannot be easily displaced. Provide protective fences or railings at the top of all retaining walls and ramps to underground garages, where a fall would be dangerous. Avoid hard paving at the bottom of retaining walls for the same reason.

Steep slopes are tempting for sliding or tobogganing, and those which lead down to busy roads should be adequately fenced, preferably at the top of the slope.

Use ornamental pools and fountains only with great care. They are not suitable where there are very young children unless they are out of reach and the water is a purely decorative film not more than a few inches deep. In all cases, pools should be located well away from walks, preferably on a separate level, and should be clearly visible to residents and passers-by.

Roof gardens should be protected by a non-climbable railing or other wall at least 1.2 m (4 ft.) high. Planters or flower beds around the edge will keep people away from the perimeters. The use of loose cobbles or objects which can be dropped over the edge should be avoided.

Transformers and other electrical equipment should be well protected, preferably in a complete enclosure rather than a chain-link cage. All elevator, boiler, and air-conditioning equipment rooms should be securely locked. Where maintenance equipment is used, a securely locked storage unit will deter children from playing with dangerous equipment.

Porches, balconies, terraces, copings, window wells, and other elevations or depressions should be surrounded by railings, closed with banisters, or otherwise protected. Gratings should be provided for sunken basement window areaways and tree wells.

Entrances should have wide roof overhang or porches for protection from rain or snow. Swing-out (awning and casement) windows should not project over walks or other traffic areas.

Lawn Mower Safety

RISK FACTORS
- In North America, lawn mowers (electric, gas-powered and riding mowers) account for an accidental injury rate of .128 per 100,000. Gas non-riding power mowers account for 22% of these accidents.

CONTRIBUTING FACTORS
- contact with moving blade
- burns
- fire
- electrical shock

COMMENT

Lawn mowers are powerful machines. They can easily sever a human finger, or hurl an object 24 m (80 ft.) or further at a speed of over 320 km/h (200 mph). Over the years, there have been some safety improvements to gas-powered mowers, such as the "dead-man" handle control (which the operator must grip to keep the blade spinning) and a blade recessed enough from the perimeter of the deck that a human foot pushed under the deck won't come into contact with it.

There is no guard or safety device that is perfect, however, and the best safety device available is still common sense.

It is not advisable to let children younger than their early teens use a power mower. Every parent must judge the strength and maturity of her/his own children, but should keep in mind that, with the possible exception of a chain saw, the lawn mower is probably the most dangerous device around the home.

SAFETY SENSE

- Mow grass only when it is dry. Wet grass increases clogging, makes a foot slip more likely, and increases the danger of shock from the power cord on an electric mower.
- If you do have a clog, never use your fingers to clear the chute. Shut off the engine, then use a stick. If you tip the mower to clean under the deck, disconnect the spark plug wire;

a hot engine can fire unexpectedly.
- Avoid pulling backward; you can pull the mower over your foot, or your foot can slip forward under the deck as you brace it to pull.
- Never mow up and down a hill with a walk-behind mower; it's too easy to slip. Always mow across a slop instead.
  (**NOTE:** Do just the opposite with a

riding mower or tractor -- mow up and down -- to reduce the risk of tipping.)

- Start the mower at a level, uncluttered spot near where you will begin mowing. Place one foot firmly on the deck, hold the handle if you can for balance, and pull the rope with the other hand. Don't let the deck lift off the ground or jump toward your foot.
- Set the height before you mow. It should be at least 5 cm (2 in.); the "billiard table" effect is not good for the grass, the blade, or the operator. A higher setting lessens the chance of striking objects and expelling them.
- Follow the service and storage instructions in the owner's manual. Draining and recapping the plug, oiling the cylinder, and washing the filter in the fall will help avoid the aggravation -- and resulting accidents -- of a hard-to-start motor in the spring.
- Protect your feet as much as possible. Steel-capped safety shoes are the best. At the very least, wear sturdy leather shoes with threaded soles. Canvas sneakers, sandals or clogs, and bare feet are never appropriate for mowing.
- Clear your lawn of foreign objects before mowing. While working, keep a sharp lookout ahead for dog bones, clothespins, sticks and stones, tree nuts, etc., that you may have missed.
- Keep in mind the location of permanent obstacles, such as cast iron valve boxes for gas and water lines, sewer cleanouts, sockets for clotheslines, bird feeders, and pop-up sprinklers. Such solid obstacles, hidden by long grass, can shatter a blade and hurl jagged fragments great distances.

- Keep children far away and watch the direction the discharge chute is aimed -- remember that the operator is in less jeopardy from thrown objects than bystanders.
- Store gas in an approved container (one with an Underwriters' Laboratory label) outside the house. Fill the mower in the open air and wipe off spills. Don't smoke while mowing. If you run out of gas before the job is done, let the engine cool before refilling.
- Unless an electric mower is double insulated, the power cord should be of the three-wire type with a grounding plug. Replace it if it shows wear, or there are breaks in the insulation. Wet conditions add to the danger.
- Be sure the cord on an electric mower never gets in the path of the blade. Some models have flip-over handles that let you reverse direction without turning, so the cord can be kept on the mowed side.
- Install a ground fault circuit interrupter (GFCI) to provide protection against electrical shock.
- Keep clear of mower exhaust. The muffler gets very hot and can burn an unwary leg. The burn, while seldom serious, is painful and can leave a deep scar.

Heat Stress

RISK FACTORS
- Over 200 people die every year in North America as a consequence of heat stress or heat stroke.

CONTRIBUTING FACTORS
- loss of body water
- strenuous work
- sun stroke

COMMENT

Hot weather makes most of us tired or irritable. Worse yet, the heat can make some people sick -- it can even kill. Your reaction to hot weather will vary depending on what shape you are in and what you do; older people, small children and very active young people are among those most at risk in the heat.

Here's how hot weather strains your ability to cope. The body itself produces metabolic heat -- more heat if you're jogging, working hard or digging in the garden than resting on a lounge chair. Outdoors on a sunny day, radiant energy adds heat to the body. If the air is warmer than your body temperature, further heat may be added. The body's heat regulation system tries to maintain a fairly constant temperature of about 37° C (98° F). The heart pumps blood from the body core to the extremities -- arms and legs -- where heat is transferred to the air. The body also gets rid of heat through the cooling evaporation of sweat. On a very hot day, when the air is no cooler than your skin, sweating may be the only means for the body to cool itself.

SAFETY SENSE

- Avoid heavy activity during the hottest part of the day. Stay inside or in the shade and relax. Joggers should run early in the morning or in the evening.
- Slow your pace and take frequent breaks to help you cool down. You simply can't expect as much of your body when temperatures are high.
- Be sure to drink enough water or other fluids. People often do not realize they are becoming dehydrated until too late.
- Avoid alcoholic drinks, since alcohol further depletes your body fluids.
- Even if you sweat a lot, don't take salt tablets. They can be dangerous, especially for those with high blood pressure. Physicians today feel that most people get adequate salt in their diets and do not need extra salt to replace what is lost in sweat.
- Wear loose, light clothing that allows sweat to evaporate and reflects the sun's rays. Do not strip to bare skin; you will not be as cool, and can get a painful sunburn. Add a hat for further protection.

70

Snowblowers

RISK FACTORS

• In North America, snowblowers injure approximately four persons per year. This translates into an accident injury rate of .036 per 100,000.

CONTRIBUTING FACTORS

• thrown debris
• hand or fingers caught in rotating auger
• frostbite

COMMENT

Snowblowers, like lawn mowers, are powerful machines that seem to hold a special attraction for pre-teens. Adults should not succumb to the pleas of children to operate the snowblower unless they are sure the youngsters have enough co-ordination -- and sheer body weight -- to effectively control the machine.

SAFETY SENSE

• Read the instruction manual and know your machine thoroughly. Keep your snowblower properly maintained, frequently checking all fasteners, guards, and parts. On electric models, check the power cord regularly for fraying or other wear.
• Do not engage a crank-type starter before you are ready to begin. If possible, disengage all drive clutches before starting.
• If the discharge chute gets clogged, shut off and disconnect power before attempting to clear it.
• Do not work after daylight unless you have very good artificial light.
• Ask onlookers to stand well back from working area.
• Always push a snowblower, don't pull it.
• Watch your footing, especially when working on an incline.
• Stop the machine if you must leave it unattended, even for a moment.

Also, shut off power if moving from one level to another or lifting or tipping the machine.
• Dress warmly for the job. But avoid long scarves or other loose-fitting clothes that might get caught in moving parts.
• If you have gravel or crushed rock surfaces, do not try to remove all snow from them; the snowblower may send bits of stone flying at high speed. Adjust the height to 2 to 3 cm (1 in.) above such potential projec-tiles.
• Stop the engine before you clean, adjust, or repair your snowblower. If the engine is gasoline powered, disconnect the spark plug; if electric, unplug the power cord.
• Wait until the engine is not only off, but cool before adding fuel. Always store fuel in an approved safety container outdoors. Remember that gasoline is extremely hazardous and ignites easily.

Chemical Lawn and Garden Care

RISK FACTORS
- Approximately 35 people die in North America each year of poisoning from agriculture, horticulture and pharmaceutical preparations.

CONTRIBUTING FACTORS
- inhalation of chemicals
- ingestion
- absorption

COMMENT

A pesticide is any substance used to kill or control unwanted rodents, plants or insects. Because pesticides are so common, we may tend to think of them as harmless. In fact, these products can pose a serious risk to our health and our environment, if they are not handled responsibly.

During warmer seasons, you should inform neighbors as to the time and location you plan to do yard and garden spraying. This will allow those who may be highly sensitive to the effects of pesticides to take precautions, and help parents ensure that their children do not play near the spraying.

If you are using a contract service, ask the service representative for a copy of the *Health and Safety Data Sheet*, which chemical companies provide to the contractors. This information sheet lists precautions that will help avoid contamination and explains what to do if you suffer an adverse reaction to the chemicals.

SAFETY SENSE

- Store pesticides in a locked, ventilated compartment, out of reach of children and well away from food, medicine or other household supplies.
- Read labels carefully for instructions about safe application, clean-up and first aid.
- When applying pesticides, wear protective clothing such as gloves to prevent contact with skin.
- When finished, wash hands and any exposed skin with soap and water. Ensure that any clothing which might have come in contact with the pesticide is washed separately from other clothes.
- Never eat or smoke while using pesticides.

- Keep children far from any area where you are applying pesticides.
- Remove food, dishes and utensils before using pesticides in the kitchen. Recover shelving with foil or new shelf paper before replacing dishes to avoid contact with left over pesticide residual.
- Always mix pesticides outdoors or in a well-ventilated area. Never use the kitchen sink or eating utensils to do the mixing.
- If you are applying a pesticide in an enclosed area, follow the directions on the label concerning ventilation of the area.
- Buy only as much pesticide as you need. Store unused amounts in the original container if you will use it in the future; if not, take it to a hazardous waste drop-off location.
- Do not re-use empty pesticide containers or burn them, since they may give off toxic fumes.
- If a pesticide is accidentally swallowed, call the Poison Control Center or your doctor immediately. If it spills on your skin, flush with water immediately.
- If a pesticide is spilled on the ground, follow the instructions on the label for clean-up. Notify the appropriate local agency if it enters a water-source or in any way contaminates the environment.

Trees and Shrub Trimming

RISK FACTORS
- Power hedge trimmers, such as small electric chain saws, injure approximately 5,000 people every gardening season in North America.

CONTRIBUTING FACTORS
- improper use of equipment
- lack of protective equipment and clothing
- improper use of ladders
- poor housekeeping in work area

COMMENT

The usual reports of injuries from this type of tool are amputated fingers, serious cuts on fingers and hands, and cuts on knees and legs from lowering the trimmer to rest the arms. Other hazards include shocks and short circuits from frayed cords or inferior extension cords.

All portable electrical equipment should contain a built-in ground wire with a polarized plug and receptacle. This protection is necessary to prevent shock if the equipment is used in wet grass or hedges.

SAFETY SENSE

- Make sure you have long enough heavy duty extension cord; never use ordinary indoor extension cord for a power trimming tool.
- Wear safety goggles when using a rotary-type trimmer with whirling circular blades; it may throw cuttings and twigs.
- Hold clippers in position ready for use before switching them on. Use both hands to hold and guide clippers.
- Always shut off current when resting arms, or picking off cuttings, or before changing direction of cut. If the trimmer becomes jammed or fails to start, always turn off the switch before looking for the trouble.
- Shut off the current and disconnect the plug if you have to leave, even for a moment. Take the clipper with you if there are children nearby.
- Keep children well away from the area while trimming.
- It is recommended that the new "U" shaped grinding slot receptacle and plug be used.
- Carry cutting tools (including hedge cutters or pruning shears) at about a 45 degree angle, with the blade or point fac-ing downward. When possible, keep sharp edges sheathed.

- To prevent an injury from a falling scythe or sickle, never leave them hanging on a shelf or rack.
- Wear gloves to prevent blisters or injuries from thorny bushes and plants.
- When trimming trees, do not carry tools while climbing. Pull them up on a rope after reaching a good working position. Place the ladder firmly and lash it in place if necessary. Test each climb before trusting your weight on it. Cut off dead limbs on the way up so there will be less danger in descending. Be sure there is no one below who could be injured by falling branches.
- Do not prune or work in trees that overlap power lines or other energized equipment.
- When cleaning up the yard after a heavy storm, etc., be on the alert for fallen wires. Do not touch them. The power or light company should handle all such jobs.

Gardens

RISK FACTORS
- One person out of 1,000 will be seriously injured each year by hand garden tools in North America.

CONTRIBUTING FACTORS
- lifting garden equipment and materials improperly
- failure to maintain and store equipment properly
- failure to check equipment before using
- lack of proper protective clothing and equipment

COMMENT

Garden work appeals to many people as an outdoor activity that brings them close to the soil. Enthusiastic gardeners should, however, remember to take it easy, especially at the beginning. In early spring, your skin will be tender and blisters may develop easily. If you overdo, sore and aching muscles, sunburned back or even more serious penalties may be your reward.

For a starter, select some lighter jobs. Short sessions of raking, stooping, lifting and carrying are a good way to condition yourself for strenuous garden activities later in the season. Avoid scooping up piles of rubbish with your hands; use a shovel.

Tools should also be conditioned before major gardening starts. The cutting edge of a spade, hoe or cultivator should be sharpened with a file. Inspect the handles of garden tools to make sure they are free of splinters that might cause wounds and invite infection.

Although hoes and rakes are simple tools, they should be handled carefully, especially where more than one person is working in a small area. Do not allow children -- or anyone inexperienced -- to use them.

SAFETY SENSE

- Examine tools for leaks, loose connections, loose fittings, etc., before using them.
- Store tools and accessories so they do not pose a tripping or cutting hazard to anyone passing in and out of a garage or a shed.
- Always shut off power tools before cleaning, adjusting, oiling, or refuelling them.
- Store only small quantities of fuel in approved containers, tightly capped

and plainly marked.
- For tips about pesticides, see page 72 in the Yard Section.
- For tips about lawn mowers, see page 68 in the Yard Section.
- Carry rakes and other long tools in your hands, not over your shoulder.
- Keep children and pets well away from power tools, and from hand tools with sharp blades.
- Always return tools to their proper places at the end of the day.
- Never leave a hoe, rake, fork, etc., lying on the ground. This is especially dangerous when the cutting edge or head is pointed upward. The sharp edges may puncture or cut through a thin-soled shoe and cause a foot injury, and/or the handle may fly up and hit a person in the face.
- Replace split, broken or sharp-edged tool and wheel-barrow handles to avoid splinter or other wounds. Sandpaper wooden handles which become weathered and rough.
- For any yard or garden work requiring reaching to the ground, don't bend. Do the job by squatting-and-straightening -- that is, keeping the back straight and using the leg muscles as much as possible.

House Maintenance

RISK FACTORS
• Falls from ladder scaffolding, from roofs and into holes account for nine percent of all home fall injuries in North America.

CONTRIBUTING FACTORS
• falls
• slips
• tripping
• incorrect lifting and carrying of loads
• falling objects

COMMENT

For many people, the arrival of spring and the return of warmer weather means yard work and outdoor repairs. But working around winter's debris and climbing up on ladders for painting, window washing and repair work can lead to the biggest cause of home deaths -- falls.

SAFETY SENSE

• Never stand on the top step of a ladder. This makes the ladder unsteady and leaves you with no handhold. Stop at the second highest step of a stepladder, or the third highest on a straight ladder.
• Don't reach out too far while on a ladder. Keep your body centered between the rails. If your belt buckle is outside the rails, you are unbalanced.
• Set your ladder on boards if the ground is soft. Wide, flat boards will keep the feet from sinking in, and tipping the ladder to one side.
• Don't place a ladder at too steep an angle. Make sure the distance from the ground to the resting point is four times the distance point from the ladder base to the structure.

• Never work on a roof or clean windows in the presence of high winds, rain, or electrical storms.
• Never climb on a wet or frosty roof.
• Wear soft-soled shoes for roof work. On a dry roof, rubber soles will provide grip so you can keep your footing. Shoes with shoelaces are the best -- they don't slip off your feet.
• Don't climb a ladder with wet or muddy shoes. Your feet could slip off the rungs and send you flying.
• Fill in cracks in sidewalks to prevent falls.
• Mark roof tripping hazards, such as plumbing vents, with a newspaper. When you step near the vent and on the paper, the change in the noise from your footing will alert you that a hazard is near.

- Don't carry storm windows up or down a ladder. If the wind catches the window, you could be pulled off the ladder. Instead, tie a rope to the window and pull it up from inside the house.
- There's also a danger of children or others being hurt by falling objects from the roof or ladder, so it's important that the neighborhood gang doesn't stand beneath you watching wide-eyed.
- Inspect your ladders every time you use them. Look for loose or broken rungs, sharp edges and splinters. Replace defective ladders.

COTTAGES AND CABINS

Because of our improved roads and the addition of more long holiday weekends in the year, increasing numbers of city dwellers are acquiring and maintaining their own private retreats. Whether lake cottages, mountain cabins, hunting lodges or fishing shacks, they are all, essentially, second homes. And how safe are we in these second homes that we see at such infrequent intervals, often for only a short time?

Chances are that people are in more danger of having an accident in their secondary than in their primary homes. For one thing, the unfamiliar surroundings of the second home may increase the possibility of accidents. Also, these dwellings are often treated as "second hand" or "second rate" homes, and do not get the attention that the city home gets. It becomes a poor relation, furnished and fitted with the castoffs from more favored rival. Repairs and improvements to the heating system, electrical wiring, floors and walks, outbuildings and furnishings may also receive "B" priority rating when compared to the same features in the first home.

The building or buildings of a vacation residence often lack the built-in safety of a city home. The rural jurisdiction may have had no building code at the time it was built, and if it has one today it may go unenforced or be out of date. Or perhaps the present structure has undergone an extensive transformation, having been added to, remodelled, "restored," winterized, etc., without the local code authority inspecting it. Nor is it uncommon to find that a second home originally was a stable, chicken coop or other structure moved from another site.

The accident probability may also be enhanced by the geographic location of the second home. Mountain and northern locations experience heavy snows that weaken structures, as well as damage from windstorms and flooding. Building materials deteriorate faster in regions of high humidity and abundant rain because of accelerated corrosion and rot. In addition, hazards associated with mountain heights and deep, swift bodies of water claim lives every year.

Travelling To and From

RISK FACTORS
- About two-thirds of all motor vehicle deaths occur on rural highways.
- Forty-five percent of all motor vehicle deaths occur between May and September.

CONTRIBUTING FACTORS
- travelling too fast for road and weather conditions
- unsafe passing on hills and curves
- alcohol

COMMENT

The majority of travelling to and from cottages takes place on rural, often isolated roads. You might think because there are fewer cars travelling on these roads that driving is safer than travelling on freeways and city streets, but this is not true. You are likely to encounter just about anything, from slow-moving farm implements and uncontrolled intersections to drunk drivers and wild animals -- any of which can present a hazard. In fact, statistics show that there is more risk of a serious traffic accident in rural areas.

SAFETY SENSE

- Watch well down the road for potential hazards, such as trucks, slow-moving vehicles, and animals. Adjust your speed accordingly.
- Be aware that visibility may be reduced at some rural intersections due to high grass, crops, or other vegetation. Reduce speed and increase attention accordingly.
- Always obey speed signs posted at curves. Remember that winding roads and hills reduce visibility.
- Adjust your speed on rural highways depending on posted limits and weather and road conditions.
- When meeting other vehicles on rural highways, be aware that safety depends on being seen, keeping to the right side of the road, and being aware of where you can drive your vehicle in case another vehicle suddenly appears in your lane.
- Learn to judge the speed and distance of oncoming cars before passing by timing oncoming cars. Before passing, ask yourself if the pass is really necessary.
- Do not attempt to pass on an incline or a curve, when approaching an intersection or railway crossing, or at other locations where visibility and space are reduced.
- When you are being passed by another vehicle, it is a courtesy to move over to the right side of the lane and slightly reduce speed to allow the other driver to complete the pass.
- Never drink if you are going to drive.

Water Safety

RISK FACTORS
- Twenty-three percent of all drownings fatalities result from small boat accidents.

CONTRIBUTING FACTORS
- falling from boat
- alcohol
- fire
- bad weather
- swimming without a "buddy"
- hypothermia
- water skiing without observer

COMMENT

Swimming, boating and fishing are the fun things to do at the cottage or during a camping trip, but enjoying water sports safely involves careful attention to possible hazards.

Avoid swimming in unfamiliar water unless someone who knows the area can assure you that it is uncontaminated and free from rapid currents, whirlpools, deep holes, rocks and other hazards. As with any strenuous activity, a physical examination prior to summer swimming is a good idea. For adults living a sedentary life, a thorough medical examination should be a prerequisite.

Most boat and fishing accidents involve capsizing and/or falling overboard.

When waterskiing, remember you need two people in the tow boat: a driver and a skier observer. Always wear a Personal Floating Device (PFD), even if you are a good swimmer.

SAFETY SENSE

- Keep a safe distance from other anglers; their movements may endanger you.
- Make sure there is ample room for backcasting. Never cast over anyone's head.
- Never leave children alone in the water. Even children who can swim can be at risk of drowning.

- Never rely on floating toys, air mattresses or arm bands to protect children from drowning.
- Don't allow a sick or tired child, or one who is taking strong medication, to go into the water.
- Arrange for your children to learn how to swim from a qualified instructor; children as young as six months can

start learning water safety.

- Don't allow swimming during thunderstorms.
- Supply enough personal flotation devices (PFDs) for all passengers when you go boating. Be sure the children's PFDs fit them correctly. It is a good idea to have children wear PFD's while even playing in or near water.
- Be sure that your boat and motor are a safe, compatible match.
- Never swim alone. Use the "buddy-system": Swim only when accompanied by another person who will keep an eye on you, and vice versa.
- Know your limitations -- do not swim when you are tired, overheated, or chilled.
- Keep away from swiftly-moving water and watch out for an undertow. If caught in a current, swim with it and at the same time angle toward shore.
- Keep hands off of others while in deep water. Do not venture into deep water unless you know how to swim, tread water, float, and turn around.

RISK FACTORS
• No North American data available.

CONTRIBUTING FACTORS
• carbon monoxide poisoning
• poisoning from plants and spoiled food
• cuts from sharp objects
• burns from campfires
• sunburn

COMMENT

More and more families are enjoying the pleasures of camping and outdoor life. Some preplanning will make camping trips both more enjoyable and safer.

Make sure that everything you take is in good condition and functioning properly. Test all equipment in your backyard or a nearby area: set up the tent, light lanterns, test the stove, etc. If you are a first-time camper, you may also want to take a "shakedown" trip nearby before trying a more ambitious adventure.

Look for a campsite that is well drained, with a good combination of sun and shade. Check the area for hazards, and instruct your children about places and things to avoid, such as poisonous plants, wild animals and moving vehicles.

SAFETY SENSE

• Wear shoes, sandals, or moccasins at the campsite; glass, cans, sharp rocks and hot embers can hurt bare feet.
• If you bring perishable food, use a portable ice chest to keep it from spoiling. If you suspect that food is tainted, get rid of it.
• Keep the site clean. Dispose of cans, bottles and garbage safely in a campground trash can, roadside refuse barrel, or community dump.
• Look for a posted indication of a water source's purity. If you have any doubts, don't drink it without boiling it or using water purification tablets.
• Obey signs and warnings concerning wildlife. If raccoons, skunks, porcupines or similar animals come to your campsite, you can scare them away with a flashlight, a fire or a loud noise. Don't keep your food in your tent where it can be smelled by the animals. Keep it stored away from the campsite.
• Light wood fires in authorized areas

only, and downwind from your campsite. Clear away leaves and other combustible material. Avoid loose clothing, which can ignite, or bathing suits, which expose skin to flame and sparks. Keep children away from the fire.

- Never leave a fire unattended. When finished with it, spread the burned pieces, soak them thoroughly with water, then cover with sand.
- Before going into a forested area, check the fire hazard index with the park rangers. Help prevent forest fires by watching your smoking habits. Smoke only in designated areas and never while walking.
- Before leaving camp to hike, boat, etc., listen to radio weather reports. Never seek shelter from a lightning storm under a tree; stay in a ditch or a low place and wait until it's over.
- Refer to page 217 of the Specialty Topics section for picnicking safety sense.

Poisonous Snakes and Plants

RISK FACTORS
- About four percent of all deaths attributed to natural and environmental factors involve death from poisoning by toxic reaction to venomous animals and plants.

CONTRIBUTING FACTORS
- animal bites
- failure to recognize dangerous snakes and plants
- allergic reaction to certain plants and insects
- failure to wear protective clothing when hiking

COMMENT

Of the over 130 species of snakes in North America, only about 19 are poisonous and can be classified into four groups: rattlesnakes, copperheads, water moccasins, and coral snakes. If your cabin or camping trip is located in an area known for snakes, read up on poisonous snakes in your local library and learn the basic first aid for treating a snake bite. Remember that a snake will not attack a man if it has a chance to escape. A number of myths exist about dangerous snakes: that a snake will not pass over a horsehair rope, that rattlesnakes always rattle before they strike, and that rattlers will not be found near black snakes. These beliefs are completely false.

There are more than 60 varieties of plants in North America that may cause irritation to the skin. Most people are immune to the effect of the majority of these plants, but nearly everyone who touches poison ivy, poison oak or poison sumach is affected to some degree. The number of cases of irritation that are due to the poison of these plants is not known. Some people are extremely resistant to the irritation caused by these plants, but this resistance is not an immunity and may vary from time to time.

SAFETY SENSE

- Carry a flashlight or lantern at night in areas where snakes are likely to be encountered. Many snakes prowl at night.
- Take care when climbing rock piles, remember that snakes often lie in rock crevices or under stones.

- In snake country, it's a good idea to wear high leather boots, puttees, or leggings; 75 percent of all snake bites are in the lower extremities. Be cautious, however, it is possible for a snake to bite through leather and inflict a wound.

- Always carry a small, handy snake-bite kit in risky areas.
- In case of a bite, have the victim remain as quiet as possible; over-exertion may speed the venom's travel toward the heart.
- Call a physician immediately. If unavailable, contact your nearest poison control center.
- Learn to recognize poisonous plants and to stay away from them.
- If you know you have brushed against a poisonous plant, wash the affected area immediately with a thick lather of soap and water. Plant poison is rapidly absorbed and fixed in the skin so that it cannot be removed.
- When going into an area where you are likely to find these plants, cover as much of your body as possible: wear long sleeves tucked into heavy leather gauntlet gloves, slacks or trousers tucked in boots or leggings, and shirt collar turned up or a scarf tied around the neck.
- Dry-clean clothing because after a bout of plant poison, soap and water are not always effective in removing the poison.

Lost in the Woods

RISK FACTORS
- Emergency and rescue teams respond to some 600 calls each year in North America. One study found that about two-thirds of lost people are between the ages of ten and 19.

CONTRIBUTING FACTORS
- extreme exposure to weather
- falls
- drowning
- panic

COMMENT

One doesn't need to be wandering in trackless back country to get lost. A wilderness emergency could happen just about anywhere a person suddenly loses those things she/he relies upon for comfort and security.

Search and rescue experts have outlined typical feelings and reactions of people when lost. Even familiar places may look strange. The lost person will feel compelled to press on, to hurry and find "the right place." As a sense of helplessness grows, she/he may race around frantically -- and uselessly -- and may discard equipment, even clothing. The sense of time may be completely lost. This panicked reaction often leads the lost person to not respond to searchers or even to hide from them.

Children may not respond because they are afraid of strangers, or afraid they will be punished for causing trouble. They may perceive the searchers' shouting as anger. Searchers draped with ropes and blaring walkie-talkies, equipped at night with headlamps, may even appear as monsters. But if you teach yourself and your child now that searchers will help you, that you can survive being lost, you can increase your chances of being among the 96 per cent of search subjects found alive.

SAFETY SENSE

- Before setting out hiking or camping, prepare a bare-bones survival kit for each person, including children. The kit should include (for those old enough to use them safely) a pocket-knife and water-proofed matches.

Other survival items:
- **A plastic trash bag, preferably brightly-colored**: This can provide an emergency shelter against the cold when worn as a poncho or stuffed leaves, grass or pine needles.

Suspended on a bush, it can provide shade from the sun in the desert. The bag can be folded and carried in a pocket or rolled up into a sausage and threaded through belt loops.

- **A whistle on a lanyard around the neck:** A child can blow a whistle longer and louder that she/he can shout, and the sound may travel farther.
- **Mirror (metal or plastic):** Sun flashes off a mirror can be seen as far as 32 km (20 mi.) away.
- **High energy food and a canteen of water:** Few searches last longer than two or three days, so starving in the wild is unlikely. But a minimal amount of food -- a handful of hard candy and some complex carbohydrates such as granola bars -- will help keep up morale as well as energy.
- **Stay put.** Searchers will begin looking for a lost person where she/he was last seen.
- **Think and rest.** Don't panic. Sit down, drink some water, and eat some food. Then ask yourself who will notice you are missing and when. Imagine what that person will do and consider how this relates to your situation.
- **Orient yourself.** Consider your surroundings and activate your survival attitude. The best survival tool is the brain.
- **Plan.** Empty your pockets and pack, look at what you have, and think about how you can use it to help yourself. Sometimes people have all the equipment they need to survive but forget about it.

The Cottage

RISK FACTORS
• No North American data available.

CONTRIBUTING FACTORS
• fire and burns
• poisoning by gases, vapors, solids, and liquids
• drowning
• firearms
• falls

COMMENT

Each and everytime you visit your cottage you should do a safety inspection to ensure that all mechanical and electrical systems and appliances are in good working order. In addition, consider the following safety sense advice.

SAFETY SENSE

• Check the cooking and heating units every time you put them back into service. Give them a complete servicing at least once a year.
• Make an escape plan and hold fire drills just like you would at home.
• Correct any mechanical and service equipment in your vacation home that you would in the primary home.
• Put guards around belts and pulleys if they are not already well encased. (Locking the room in which they are located isn't sufficient.)
• Take the doors off of discarded or unused refrigerators or, if this isn't practical, shove door side up against the wall.
• Install pressure/temperature relief valves on hot water storage tanks and pipe the discharge down near the floor.

• Ground all electrical equipment that is near a damp or wet environment or personal grounding sources, such as metal pipes and ducts. Don't forget equipment located at some distance from the cottage, such as water pumps and yard or dock lights.
• Fill in all unused excavations, such as dug wells, cisterns, quarries, open cesspools, etc.
• Replace wooden well and well-pit covers with concrete slabs that are reinforced with steel rods.
• Anchor unit heaters well so that they won't tip over. Protect their fuel lines from damage. (Never use rubber tubing.)
• Make sure that all space heating equipment is properly vented to the outside -- never into the attic -- via a vent stack or chimney.

- Use only cooking and heating equipment that bear the label of a nationally recognized testing agency. Keep them in top operating condition.
- Ask the local building inspector or a contractor to look at your cottage for built-in hazards; it may not have been built in accordance with the minimum requirements of a building code. Correct any defects.
- Reinforce the roof to withstand the ravages of weather.
- Put handrails on stairs and porches.
- Replace one-step changes in floor and walk elevations with ramps.
- Replace masonry chimneys supported by wooden wall brackets with the more modern lightweight insulated insulated ones.
- Have an electrical inspector or electrician look over the wiring, which may be unsafe and inadequate -- especially if it's been added on to.
- Install three-hole outlets and make sure they are all properly connected and grounded.
- Add more outlets if necessary to eliminate the need for extension cords and more circuits if the present ones are overloaded.
- Trim tree limbs away from service lines.
- If you have a propane refrigeration unit, be sure it is fume vented to the outdoors; these units generate carbon monoxide.

PLAY STRUCTURES AND AREAS

"They fly through the air with the greatest of ease ..." but unlike trapeze artists, kids on playground apparatus often land with the greatest of thuds -- thuds that can mean painful lacerations, broken bones, and concussions.

Can parents safeguard youngsters at play in backyards without totally eliminating risk and fun? They can if they remember the five keys to playground safety: selection, surfacing, maintenance, supervision, and kid training.

Some knowledge of child development is important for choosing and designing play areas. The type of equipment, scale, and degree of challenge should be appropriate for the age groups of the children who will use it. This type of information can usually be obtained from a public library or community recreation department.

Because 60 to 70 percent of the children who fall from playground apparatus land on the ground, it is important to provide as soft a landing surface as possible. Sand is the best choice, although grass is another option and certainly softer than concrete. Young children especially need such built-in safety factors under climbing frames and swing sets.

Any play equipment is potentially dangerous if not properly maintained. Concrete footings for fixed equipment must be set sufficiently deep to avoid their working through the surface. As rain and sun purify sand, sand boxes should not be covered; if necessary, they can be protected by wire netting from fouling by animals. Wooden climbing and play equipment should have all edges rounded to avoid splinters.

Children can hurt themselves on even the best equipment if they are not properly supervised. Swimming pools especially should be completely off limits when adults are not around. The degree of supervision necessary depends, of course, upon the age and maturity of the children. Parents should also make and enforce rules about where children can play; having the safest backyard in town will not help if your children spend their time playing by the railway tracks.

Children can and should learn what are safe places to play, how to use their equipment properly, and what not to try on it. By teaching children to play responsibly, and to call for help when they need it (and not to when they don't!), you encourage them to learn caution and common sense in other things.

Swings and Slides

RISK FACTORS
• Home playground equipment accidents account for 17 percent of all sport and recreation-related injuries in North America.

CONTRIBUTING FACTORS
• poor maintenance of equipment
• strangulation on protruding parts
• falls
• youngsters not physically capable of using equipment
• lack of sand or other absorbing material beneath equipment

COMMENT

Install playground equipment well away from "heavy traffic" areas of the yard, such as patios and walkways.

Teach your children the basics of safe play. On swings, sit in the center of the seat -- never stand or kneel. Hold on with both hands and stop the swing before getting off. Have only one person swing at a time. Never swing empty swings or twist the chains, and stay away from both the front and back of moving swings.

On slides, use the steps -- never climb up the sliding surface. Slide down feet first, sitting up, one person at a time. Be sure everyone is out of the way before sliding. Supervision is a must with home play equipment.

SAFETY SENSE

• Before starting to assemble swings or slides, read all assembly and safety instructions.
• Pinch in ends of S-hooks with pliers; open-ended hooks can catch clothing and skin.
• Cap or cut off and tape all exposed bolts and screws. Tape rough edges and sharp points with duct or electrical tape.
• Set equipment legs in concrete or anchor them with specially designed spikes. Keep either anchors or concrete below ground level to avoid a tripping hazard.
• Erect equipment, particularly swings, at least 2 m (6 ft.) from fences, building walls, walkways or other play areas, such as sandboxes. Point slide exits away from other play areas.
• Place metal slides in the shade to avoid burns.
• Nail a wood block or place used tires under each end of seesaws so children won't catch their feet if the board falls suddenly.

- Choose swing seats made of plastic, canvas, or rubber, with smooth or rounded edges. Another good option is a tire swing if it's installed properly, i.e., proper side clearance.
- Keep sand underneath equipment at least 15 cm (6 in.) deep to ensure soft landings.
- Do a maintenance check every week on playground area. Refill landing pits, level surfacing materials and remove debris.
- Select a slide with an incline of less than 30 degrees (if it's twice as long as it is high, the incline is about 26 degrees). Steps or rungs should be evenly spaced and between 18 to 27 cm (7 to 11 in.) apart.
- If a slide is over 1.2 m (4 ft.) high, be sure it has slide rails and a top barrier. The exit surface should be parallel to the ground and 38 cm (15 in.) above it.
- When the child grows beyond the age guidelines for the equipment, dismantle it. Older children put too much stress on the equipment, which can result in equipment failure and accidents.

Backyard Water Play

RISK FACTORS
• Nearly 80 percent of all home drownings occur in residential pools.

CONTRIBUTING FACTORS
• unprotected water sources
• lack of supervision
• failure to teach water safety to children

COMMENT

Swimming and water play are popular with children and adults alike. There are millions of permanent in-ground residential pools in North America, and further millions of above-ground and portable plastic pools. Unfortunately, these pools are not only the site of summer fun, but the most common location of child drownings. Even when not swimming, children are at risk. Often they simply fall into the pool while playing around it. Or they may throw things into the pool and then, while trying to retrieve them, topple in. Children have also drowned after slipping and hitting their heads on a pool deck or steps, then falling unconscious into the pool. Most drownings occur during a few minutes of inattention, with a parent or guardian only steps away. Whenever children are around water, someone should be conscientiously responsible for watching them.

SAFETY SENSE

• Teach your children to respect water. From an early age, we teach children that water is fun -- with a nightly bathing routine, for example. They may not recognize that water can kill them.
• Do not underestimate the ability of your child. If she/he can climb out of a crib, a low fence around a swimming pool is not a barrier.
• Install a fence or barrier at least 1.2 m (4 ft.) high around all four sides of home pools. The design should be without handholds or footholds so a child can't climb it. Self-closing and self-latching mechanisms on gates ensure that a gate won't carelessly be left ajar.
• Keep gates locked when the pool is not being used. Some pool owners go so far as to equip their pools with automatic alarm devices.
• Be aware that any body of water around the home is a potential drowning hazard. A child can drown in an open septic tank in the backyard.

- If the pool area is a main play area for children, buy lightweight personal flotation jackets for young swimmers to wear. If they fall in, at least there's hope for survival until rescued.
- In winter, install a rigid cover mounted on a track, bars, or metal supports to prevent falls into the pool. Consult your manufacturer for winterizing procedures.
- Place a safety float across the pool 30 cm (12 in.) or more in advance of steep bottom slopes to warn of the sudden increase in depth.
- Empty wading pools after use each day.
- Don't place chairs, tables or other objects near the barrier around the pool; a child may be able to crawl over the barrier or reach the gate latch.

- Post the numbers for emergency medical services in a conspicuous place.
- If possible, install a phone near the pool area for quick access to emergency help.
- Know how to administer artificial resuscitation.
- During rainy seasons and spring thaw, supervise youngsters carefully outdoors; they can easily fall into a stream or even a puddle. If you have extensive property, it is best to have it landscaped to prevent any accumulation of water to which children could have easy access.
- Don't assume that because a younger child is with an older child near a lake or stream that all is well. Either one may wander off to explore the area.

Climbing Structures

RISK FACTORS

• Three percent of all home deaths caused by falls occur among children aged 14 and under.

CONTRIBUTING FACTORS

• poor maintenance of equipment
• falls
• lack of sand or other absorbing material beneath structure
• children not physically capable of using equipment

COMMENT

Climbing structures (monkey bars, horizontal ladders, etc.) provide great fun for youngsters and help build self-confidence and upper body strength. There are several types of apparatus suitable for youngsters at various ages. It is important to choose a climber appropriate to your child's level, not only because this will increase her/his interest and fun, but because it strongly affects the comparative safety with which she/he uses it. In selecting an appropriate climber, remember that size and motor development are as important as age in determining whether a youngster will be able to enjoy it safely.

SAFETY SENSE

• For very young children, provide a simple structure of interconnected bars. The area under the structure should be surfaced with a soft, resilient material like sand.
• Teach youngsters the proper grip, with the thumb encircling the bar opposite the fingers. They should hold on with both hands, except while moving to a new position.
• Do not allow overcrowding on a climber.
• For primary and intermediate children, supply horizontal ladders and bars, making sure that the bars of the apparatus are low enough that

children can reach them unaided. If a child must stand on a box to reach a climber or be lifted, she/he is too small for it.
• If several children are playing on horizontal bars and ladders, ensure that they start at the same end of the apparatus and move in the same direction, keeping a safe distance between them and watching out for swinging feet.
• Do not allow any kind of speed contests on the apparatus or trying to cover large distances in a single move.
• Teach children how to drop, landing

on their feet with knees slightly bent.
- Check climbing structures weekly. Test all connections to make certain that bars will not turn; keep the surfacing material level and at least 15 cm (6 in.) deep.
- Do not allow children to play on climbing structures (including bars, rings, and horizontal ladders) that are not absolutely dry.
- Ensure that there are no protruding bolts. If a child slips, clothing can catch on the bolt, hanging the child.
- Do not allow children to wear loose-fitting clothing while using the structure.

Wheeled Toys

RISK FACTORS
• North American data on injuries by toy vehicles are not available, but it is estimated that some 250 children each year are killed in accidents involving toy vehicles.

CONTRIBUTING FACTORS
• poorly constructed or designed toys
• unstable tricycles
• collisions with obstacles
• inability to stop tricycle
• wagons being pulled or pushed too fast
• failure to slow wagons down before turning corners
• wagons on roadways

COMMENT

So much has been written on the danger of playing on streets, highways and driveways that cautions against this practice are limited only by the amount of space we can give to the subject. Bear in mind, too, that some games played on the sidewalks are also dangerous. For instance, any game involving a ball or other object which could roll or fall into the street will lead to children chasing out into the street to retrieve it, which may be just as fatal as playing in the street in the first place.

However, there are some basic safety sense tips for the use of tricycles and wagons that, if followed, will prevent some accidents.

SAFETY SENSE

• Never allow standing up in a wagon. The center of gravity becomes too high for good balance, and the wagon may overturn.
• Have children keep arms and legs inside the wagon sides. Many injuries result when limbs extend beyond the sides.
• Do not push or pull a wagon fast when there is a person on board. The wagon may overturn, particularly when going around a corner.
• Teach children never to coast down a hill or driveway into the road.
• Don't hitch a wagon to a bicycle. The swaying of the wagon may cause it to overturn.
• Match the size of the tricycle to the size of the child. If a trike is too small, it will be unstable. If it is too big, its rider may have difficulty controlling it properly.
• Keep in mind that low-slung tricycles with seats close to the ground, such as "Big Wheels," offer more stability, as do tricycles with wheels that are

spaced widely apart.

- Watch out for sharp edges on tricycles, particularly on fenders. Cover any sharp edges and protrusions with heavy, waterproof tape.
- Advise your child to keep hands and feet away from moving spokes.
- Look for pedals and handgrips with a rough surface to prevent the child's hands and feet from slipping.
- Keep the tricycle in good condition. Don't leave it outdoors overnight; moisture can cause rust and weaken metal parts.
- Do not allow children to ride double. Carrying a passenger on a tricycle makes it much less stable.
- Caution your child against riding down hills. A tricycle can pick up so much speed that it becomes almost impossible to stop.
- Teach your child to slow down when turning and not to ride down steps or over curbs.

Unauthorized Play Areas

RISK FACTORS
- Ten percent of all public railway deaths occur to children under 14 years of age.
- Twenty-seven percent of all public drownings (away from home, and excluding boats) occur to children under 14 years of age.

CONTRIBUTING FACTORS
- trespassing on railway projects
- playing in ditches with water
- suffocation from cave-ins

COMMENT

Every day we hear of children injured or killed while playing in ditches, sewers, empty houses, railway yards, etc. Parents have the responsibility to make clear to children what areas are and are not safe to play in, and to impress upon them that it is not only forbidden but dangerous to play in unauthorized areas. Remember, also, that the more attractive and interesting play spaces are provided around the home and neighborhood, the less tempted children will be to stray to forbidden places.

SAFETY SENSE

- **Ditches and excavations:** Digging operations always invite an accident. A cave-in or a falling overhang could suffocate or crush a person. Falling into an excavation might result in broken bones.
- **Construction work:** The hazards of construction sites are too numerous and obvious to mention. Make it clear to children that playing in and around such sites is not only very dangerous, it's trespassing.
- **Empty houses:** Entering them is both illegal and dangerous. Broken windows may cause serious cuts; rotten stairs or floors may collapse; and there is danger of tripping or falling over unseen objects.
- **Wharves, piling, barges, etc.:** The danger of slipping, falling, drowning and crushing accidents is always present in such areas. Other unsuitable places include jetties, rock piles, etc., in resort areas near beaches. This is a serious hazard, particularly for youngsters who are surf fishing without adult supervision.
- **Sawdust piles:** Large piles of sawdust are left standing in certain sections of the country where there are logging and sawmill operations. Although they look harmless, burning without flame may be taking place underneath, in which case any

pressure will cause it to collapse and burst into flames.

• **Quarries:** A quarry is a place where stone for building is dug out. It is often very deep, sometimes 30 m (100 ft.) or more, and underground springs or rain fill it with water. Quarry depths are made up of jagged rock and hard surface. A child can have a fatal fall, be hit by falling rocks, or be injured by blasting operations and blasting caps. Deep pools are another hazard; tempted to swim in them, children may drown or be struck by rocks submerged near the surface.

• **Railway tracks and trains:** Children may fall under cars while hopping rides on trains; be hit by a train while crossing or walking on or near railway tracks; be trapped by a train on trestles and bridges; fall off boxcars while climbing on them; be crushed by materials inside cars.

• **Mines and pits:** Children may think it exciting to explore such areas, risking being crushed if rotten timber posts collapse, breathing bad (poisonous) air, falling down deep holes, etc.

Junk

RISK FACTORS
• No North American data available.

CONTRIBUTING FACTORS
• confinement in a closed space
• failure to wear foot protection
• crushed by rolling equipment and materials

COMMENT

Backyard junk is often the number one play toy for North American youngsters. Such items as tin cans, broken glass, lawnmowers, knives, garden tools, pieces of pipe, old cars, old wood with nails, refrigerators, etc., are often more attractive to children than safety-tested toys. Keep your yard clean of dangerous items and provide children with safe alternatives to play with.

SAFETY SENSE

• Select toys for preschool children that are simple, have no detachable or breakable small parts. Objects such as saucepans, wooden spoons, large empty spools, soft plastic containers and empty cardboard boxes are safe, available tools for back yard and sand box play.
• Beware of the hazards of refrigerators and freezers, whether abandoned or used outside for summer storage of food. If a fridge is abandoned, remove the doors so children cannot become trapped in it. If it is in use, the door should have a clasp hinge and be kept locked.
• Store garden tools and equipment in a safe place, preferably a locked storage shed. Tools such as rakes, if left hanging on fences, can fall and

severely injure a child.
• Pieces of heavy equipment or motor engines should be blocked securely to prevent them from rolling and trapping a child's leg or other body part.
• Always lock automobiles not in use, including the trunk. Many a young child has crawled into a trunk, closed the lid, and died of heat stroke or suffocation during a game of hide and seek.
• Remember that yard maintenance is a must even if you don't have children. Neighboring children may always venture onto your property, and you can be held accountable for injuries resulting from hazardous objects lying around your yard.

HAND TOOLS

Home projects that you tackle yourself can be fun and relaxing. However, using hand and power tools involves certain hazards. If you have a home workshop, you should be aware of these dangers and take care to reduce them as much as possible. Start by acquainting yourself thoroughly with the owner's manuals of your tools; get to know the applications, limitations, and hazards of each.

Weather tools and most new tools are equipped with a three-prong plug for use in a three-hole receptacle of a grounded electrical wiring system. If you have a three-prong plug and a two-hole wall receptacle, use an adaptor with a wire connection that attaches to a known ground.

Most power tools have guards that partially shield the blade or bit; these should be in place at all times when the tools are in use. When they are not in use, or when you are repairing them or changing accessories (such as bits, blades, cutters, etc.), unplug the tools completely.

Wear safety glasses or face shields where there is danger of flying fragments and dust masks when conditions warrant. Use safety footwear to reduce the risk of toe injury. Avoid wearing gloves, ties, jewelry, and loose clothing around moving machinery such as drills, saws, or grinders. Clamp or vice your work piece when using boring and cutting tools. This will free both hands to operate the tools safely.

Do not ask too much of your equipment. All powertools should be operated at the recommended rate, never forced. Failure to select the correct tool could result in personal injury and/or tool damage.

Keep work areas clean. Pick up things that can be tripping, bumping, or falling hazards. Ensure that any area where you use power tools is dry and well lit. Store tools in a safe place, out of the reach of children.

Much of the following information on powered hand tools has been extracted from Safety Infograms published by the Canadian Centre for Occupational Health and Safety.

Air-powered Tools

RISK FACTORS

• The most common air-powered tools in the home are nail guns and stud drivers. They account for some 1,500 hospital-treated injuries in North America annually.

CONTRIBUTING FACTORS

• failure to wear protective equipment, especially eye protection
• improper use of tools

COMMENT

Air-powered tools include nail and staple guns, grinders, drills, jackhammers, chipping hammers, riveting hammers and wrenches.

Their speed and power can save a lot of time and effort over hand tools, but the force they carry can also be a hazard to the user. Exercise great care and wear personal protective equipment to avoid injury in case the machine slips or breaks.

SAFETY SENSE

• Don't make air hoses into tripping hazards by laying them across walkways or curling them underfoot.
• Be sure hose connections fit properly and are equipped with a mechanical means of insuring connection (chain or wire).
• Install quick disconnects of a pressure-release type rather than disengagement type. Attach the male end of the connector to the tool, not the hose.
• Turn off air pressure to the hose when not using it or when changing tools.
• Check hoses regularly for cuts, bulges and abrasions. Replace them if necessary.
• Blow out the air line before connecting a tool: hold the hose firmly and blow away from yourself and others.
• Choose air-supply hoses that have a minimum working pressure rating of 1035 kPa (150 psi), or 150% of the maximum pressure produced in the system -- whichever is higher.
• Wear safety glasses or a face shield and, where necessary, safety shoes and hearing protection.
• Put shields up in areas where tools are used and others may be exposed to flying chips, dust, or excessive noise.
• Reduce operator fatigue. Support heavy tools by means of counter balance wherever possible.
• Avoid cleaning with compressed air whenever possible. If no alternate method is available, keep nozzle pressure below 207 kPa (30 psi). Use personal protective equipment and effective chip-guarding techniques.
• Do not use compressed air to blow debris or to clean dirt from clothes.

Drills

RISK FACTORS

- An estimated 15,000 drill-related injuries are treated annually in hospitals in North America.

CONTRIBUTING FACTORS

- failure to wear protective equipment, especially eye protection
- failure to clamp the work item

COMMENT

The hand-held electric drill with its series of attachments enables anyone to tackle a wide variety of jobs in a home workshop, from drilling and sanding to sawing, buffing, and polishing to spin-cleaning paintbrushes. Used properly, it is a valuable tool that will last for years. However, drill owners should be aware of the power of these tools and take care to avoid hazards associated with them.

SAFETY SENSE

- Wear safety glasses or a face shield when drilling.
- Keep drill vents clear to maintain adequate ventilation.
- Keep drill bits sharp at all times. Never use a bent drill bit or one that doesn't turn true.
- Keep all cords clear of the cutting area during use.
- Disconnect the power supply before changing or adjusting a bit or attachment.
- Tighten the chuck securely and remove the chuck key before starting drill.
- Secure the piece being drilled -- with clamps, not your other hand -- to keep it from slipping.
- Slow the rate of feed just before breaking through the surface.
- Drill a small pilot hole before attempting large holes.
- Do not exceed the manufacturer's recommended maximum drilling capacities.
- Do not use a hole saw cutter without the pilot drill.
- Do not use high speed steel (HSS) bits without cooling or lubrication.
- Always be sure you have proper footing and balance when drilling.
- Do not reach under or around stock being drilled.
- Select a bit or attachment suitable to the size of the drill and the work being done. Follow the manufacturer's guidelines, especially with an unfamiliar drill.

Belt Sanders and Grinders

RISK FACTORS

• Some 13,000 injuries are treated annually at hospital facilities in North America.

CONTRIBUTING FACTORS

• inhalation of dust
• failure to wear face/eye protection
• improper set-up of equipment

COMMENT

The belt sander is a type of power sanding tool available in both stationary and portable models. Belt sanders can be fitted with grinding wheels, which are handy for sharpening tools or knives and for grinding metal parts.

SAFETY SENSE

Belt Sanders

• Always wear safety glasses or a face shield when using a belt sander, and add a dust respirator for dusty operations.
• Install sanding belts that are the same width as the pulley drum.
• Disconnect the power supply before changing the sanding belt, making adjustments, or emptying the dust collector.
• Inspect a sanding belt before using it. Replace any belt that is worn or frayed.
• Adjust the sanding belt tension so it runs true and at the same speed as the pulley drum.
• Be sure the sanding belt is secured in the correct direction as indicated on the belt and the machine.
• Use two hands to operate sanders:

one on the trigger switch, the other on the front knob handle. Keep your hands away from the belt at all times.
• Do not exert excessive pressure upon the moving sander.
• Keep all cords clear of the sanding area while working.
• Clean dust from the motor and vents at regular intervals. Be careful not to cover the air vents.
• Do not use a sander without an exhaust system or dust collector. Empty the collector when it is 1/4 full.
• Do not work on unfixed stock unless it is heavy enough to stay in place. Secure the stock with clamps or a "stop block."
• Do not overreach. Ensure that you have proper footing and good balance at all times.

Grinding Wheels

- Never use a grinding wheel without both the guard and your eye protection in place.
- Be sure that the tool or work rest has a maximum clearance of 3 mm (1/8 in.) from the grinding wheel and is positioned above its center line.

- Check that the wheel has no cracks.
- Operate the grinder only at the manufacturer's recommended speed. Read the speed rating on the blotter before placing it on the grinder.
- Ring-test grinding wheels before beginning work.

Planers

RISK FACTORS

- An estimated 9,000 injuries related to planers are treated at hospitals in North America each year.

CONTRIBUTING FACTORS

- cuts from improper hand placement
- electrical shock
- foreign objects in materials being planed

COMMENT

Planers come in various types -- dado, fore, jack, jointer, rabbet, etc. Manual ones are relatively safe to use.   However, power planers can be dangerous, mainly because of the electrical connections and the increased force and speed.

SAFETY SENSE

All Planers

- Wear safety glasses or a face shield.
- Use blades of the same weight and set at exactly the same height.
- Ensure blade-locking screws are tight.
- Support the stock in a comfortable position for doing the job safely and accurately.
- Check stock thoroughly for staples, nails, screws, or other foreign objects before planing.
- Start a cut with the infeed table (front shoe) resting firmly on the stock, and the cutter head slightly behind the edge of the stock.
- Do not overreach. Be sure you have proper footing and good balance at all times.

Power Planers

- Remove any adjusting keys and wrenches before turning the power on.
- Disconnect an electrical planer from the power supply before making any adjustments to the cutter head or blades.
- Disconnect the power supply to dump out chips. Do not put a finger or any object in the deflector to clean out chips while the planer is running.
- Use two hands to operate the planer: one on the trigger switch, the other on the front handle.
- Keep all cords clear of the cutting area.
- Do not set the planer down until the blades have stopped turning.

Pneumatic Nailing and Stapling Tools

RISK FACTORS

• An estimated 3,500 injuries are treated annually at hospital facilities in North America.

CONTRIBUTING FACTORS

• failure to wear eye and hand protection
• failure to follow manufacturers' use procedures

COMMENT

Pneumatic nailing and stapling tools can be very useful in the home workshop when used correctly and carefully. However, they present a serious hazard in the hands of children. Ensure that all such tools are put away in a locked cabinet when not being used. It is also a good idea to keep staples and nails out of the reach of young children.

SAFETY SENSE

• Wear safety glasses or a face shield and, where necessary, hearing protection.
• Inspect the tool before connecting it to the air supply; be sure all screws and cylinder caps are securely tightened.
• Check that you are using the correct air supply and pressure before connecting tools.
• Check that the tool is correctly connected to its air supply and is in working order, with safety the mechanism operative, before using it.
• Always handle a pneumatic tool as if it contains fasteners, whether or not you think it actually does. Never point it towards yourself or anyone else.

• Disconnect the tool from the air supply when cleaning or adjusting it, or when leaving it unattended.
• Use only fasteners recommended by the manufacturer.
• Do not use a pressure above the manufacturer's rating.
• Do not depress the trigger unless the nose piece of the tool is directed onto a safe work surface.
• Do not transport the tool with the trigger depressed.
• Do not load the tool with fasteners when the trigger is depressed.
• Do not overreach. Make sure you have proper footing and good balance at all times.
• Do not use compressed air to blow debris or to clean dirt from clothes.

Explosive Actuated Fastening Tools

RISK FACTORS
• National data about explosive actuated fastening tools are not available. However, the power tool accounts for 28 percent of all the home workshop injuries reported at emergency treatment departments.

CONTRIBUTING FACTORS
• failure to wear face and eye protection
• failure to follow manufacturers' use procedures

COMMENT

Explosive actuated fastening tools use explosive cartridges to drive in nails, studs, or other fasteners. These cartridges must be kept away from heat and moisture, and should also be secured out of the reach of children. The force produced by the explosions is quite strong, and these tools must be operated with caution and attention to possible hazards.

SAFETY SENSE

• Wear safety glasses or a face shield, a hard hat, and hearing protection.
• Brace yourself at all times when working on ladders or scaffolds to maintain good balance.
• Always keep the tool pointed in a safe direction.
• Do not carry loaded tools from job to job.
• Do not permit bystanders in the immediate vicinity of the work. You may have to shield the working area to protect against possible ricochet.
• Clean and maintain tools in accordance with manufacturers' instructions.
• Check tools before using them; remove from service any that are not in good working order until they are

repaired.
• Check the chamber of a tool before using it to see that the barrel is clean and unobstructed.
• Store tools and cartridges in a locked container when not in use.
• Always use the tool at right angles to the work surface.
• Do not use the tool where flammable or explosive vapors, dusts, or other substances are present.
• Never place your hand over the front (muzzle) end of a loaded tool.
• Use only cartridges and projectiles (nails, studs, etc.) recommended by the tool manufacturer.
• Ensure that base material has no holes or openings and is solid enough that a projectile would not

pass right through.

- Do not load a tool until immediately before use.
- Do not leave a loaded tool unattended.
- Check that the strength of the cartridge is appropriate for the work being done; charge cartridges are color-coded according to strength.
- If you are not sure which strength cartridge to use, make a first trial fixing with the lowest-strength and work upward if it is not strong enough.
- Provide adequate ventilation when using explosive actuated tools in confined spaces.
- If a tool misfires, hold it in the fixing position for no less than 15 seconds. Keep it pointed in a direction which will not cause injuries while unloading and discarding the cartridge very carefully.
- Be very careful when using tools near live electrical circuits. Ensure fastenings do not penetrate live circuits that are buried or hidden in the base material.
- Do not attempt to force a cartridge into a tool.
- Carry cartridges in the manufacturer's package, not loose or in a pocket.

Routers

RISK FACTORS
* No North American data available.

CONTRIBUTING FACTORS
* failure to wear eye protection
* failure to secure material being worked on

COMMENT

The router is a versatile power tool capable of doing many woodworking operations. The best-known type is the portable hand electric router, which is readily adaptable as a power planer, a spindle shaper, a hinge mortiser or a dovetail machine. Whatever the application, use caution when handling this power tool, since sudden torque or kickback from the router can cause damage and injury.

SAFETY SENSE

* Wear eye protection or a face shield.
* Disconnect the power supply before making adjustments or changing bits.
* Ensure that the bit is securely mounted in the chuck and that the base is right.
* Before switching on the motor, put the base of the router on the workpiece, template, or guide and check that the bit can rotate freely.
* Secure the stock firmly. Never rely on yourself or a second person to support or hold the material.
* Check the stock thoroughly for staples, nails, screws, or other foreign objects before using a router.
* Hold both hands on the router handles at all times until the motor has stopped.
* Keep all cords clear of the cutting area.
* Do not overreach. Make sure you have proper footing and good balance at all times.
* Feed the router bit into the material at a firm, controlled speed.
* Always use a safe cutting speed as indicated by the sound of the motor: when the router is fed onto the material too slowly, the motor makes a high-pitched whine; when the router is pushed too hard, the motor makes a low growling noise.
* When the type of wood or size of the bit force you to work slowly, make two or more passes to prevent the router from burning out or kicking back.
* Do not set the router down until the exposed bit has stopped turning.

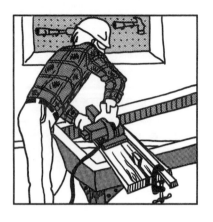

Circular Saws

RISK FACTORS

• Thirteen percent of all power saw injuries treated at hospitals yearly are attributed to portable circular power saws.

CONTRIBUTING FACTORS

• contact with blade
• electric shock
• tripping over extension cords
• dropped saws
• saw "kickback" from pinching the blade in the cut

COMMENT

Portable electrical circular saws of many different types are used by home hobbyists, construction trades, and maintenance workers. They save a lot of time in many operations, but if not used properly they can be a very dangerous tool.

The most important requirements for using this type of saw safely are proper use, frequent inspection, and a rigorous maintenance schedule. Follow the manufactuers' recommendations for operating procedures and keep a systematic inspection schedule and maintenance record. If you don't use your saw correctly and keep it in good shape, the motor is likely to get hot and burn the insulation off the windings. This almost always results in short circuit, which can cause serious injury to the user.

SAFETY SENSE

• If you are left-handed, keep in mind that circular saws are designed for right-handed operation; safe left-handed operation demands more care.
• Wear safety glasses or a face shield.
• Wear an approved respirator if the job will produce harmful or nuisance dusts.
• Use a sharp blade that is designed for your work and suitable for the stock being cut.
• Check the retracting lower blade

guard frequently to make certain it works freely. It should enclose the teeth as completely as possible, and cover the unused portion of the blade when cutting.
• Allow the saw to reach full power before cutting.
• Ensure that the retracting lower blade guard is fully returned before laying the saw down.
• Disconnect the power supply before adjusting or changing the blade.
• Keep all cords clear of the cutting

area.

- Use two hands to operate the saw: one on the trigger switch, the other on the front knob handle.
- Keep the upper and retracting lower blade guards clean and free of sawdust.
- Keep the motor free from any accumulation of dust and chips.
- Allow the blade to cut steadily; do not force it.
- Check the saw for proper blade rotation.
- Secure the work being cut to avoid movement.
- Do not hold or fix the retracting lower guard in the open position.
- Do not place a hand under the shoe or guard of the saw.
- Do not overtighten the blade-locking nut.
- Do not twist the saw to change, cut, or check its alignment.
- When "ripping" stock, use a wedge or guide that is clamped or nailed to the stock.
- If a saw vibrates or appears unsafe in any way, do not use it.
- Before cutting, check materials for obstructions or foreign objects, such as nails and screws.
- Do not carry a saw with your finger on the trigger switch.
- Do not overreach. Make sure you have proper footing and good balance at all times.

Jig Saws and Reciprocating Saws

RISK FACTORS
• No North American data available.

CONTRIBUTING FACTORS
• failure to wear eye protection
• improper securing of materials
• failure to disconnect saw after use

COMMENT

Numerous jobs can be done on a jig saw. It is an efficient machine for cutting out diagrams, figures and the like, and a relatively safe piece of equipment to use. Still, like any power tool, it can cause injury if not used with proper care.

SAFETY SENSE

• Wear safety glasses or a face shield.
• Disconnect the power supply before changing or adjusting blades.
• Use lubricants when cutting metals.
• Keep all cords clear of cutting materials.
• Position the saw before cutting. Do not insert a blade into or withdraw a blade from a cut or lead hole while the blade is moving.
• Make sure, however, that the blade is not in contact with the stock or the saw will stall when the motor starts.
• Do not start cutting until the saw reaches full power.
• Do not put down a saw until the motor has stopped.

• Secure and support the stock as close as possible to the cutting line to avoid vibration.
• Keep the base or shoe of the saw in firm contact with the stock being cut.
• Select the correct blade for the stock being cut.
• Allow the saw to cut steadily; do not force it, especially around curves.
• Do not reach under or around the stock being cut; hold the saw down firmly before switching it on.
• Drill a lead hole larger than the saw blade. With the saw switched off, insert the blade in the hole until the shoe rests firmly on the stock.

Tool Design

RISK FACTORS

• Well over 300,000 home workshop injuries a year in North America require medical attention at a hospital treatment facility. Thousands of other injuries go unreported.

CONTRIBUTING FACTORS

• using the wrong tool for the job
• using incorrect procedures for a tool
• failure to keep tools in a safe condition

COMMENT

Almost every home has a hammer, screwdriver, pair of pliers, and perhaps a handsaw and one or more wrenches. However, not every person in the home knows how to select and use hand tools or how to take proper care of them. The misuse of hand tools is the cause of many injuries in the home that could be avoided with a little care, education, and training. It is best to get instruction or advice from an experienced person before setting to work with your own tools, and to keep in mind the general tips below.

SAFETY SENSE

• Bend your elbow, not your wrist when using hammers, wrenches, or pliers.
• Select the tool with the workplace layout and job design in mind. Sometimes a tool is correct for one operation and incorrect for another.
• Keep the weight of hand tools to a minimum. Tools used often that weigh over 0.5 kg (1 lb.) should be counterbalanced. The center of gravity of the tool should be as close to the center of the grip as possible.
• With electric tools, reduce power to the lowest possible setting to complete the job. This reduces tool vibration at the source.

• Choose tools that have a high handle mass relative to the tool body. Handles should be covered with cork, rubber, or plastic, or plastic-bonded to steel. This helps to reduce vibration.
• Choose hand tools with two handles; they are easier to hold and manipulate.
• Choose tools with a trigger strip rather than trigger button. This allows the force to be spread over a greater area of the hand, reducing muscle fatigue.
• Ensure that the trigger works easily; reducing the effort needed to operate the tool.

Striking Tools

RISK FACTORS

- Some 50,000 injuries resulting from using a hammer are treated each year at North American hospitals.

CONTRIBUTING FACTORS

- striking hand and fingers
- using bent nails
- improper striking procedure

COMMENT

Striking tools have been used since prehistoric times, when early humans used rocks as hammers for simple jobs like extracting marrow from bones. Today, although the basic principle remains, there have been a few improvements in design. Two of the most widely used striking tools are the ball peen and the claw (nail) hammer, both of which are available in different sizes and weights.

Nail hammers have either curved or straight (ripping) claws designed for pulling nails and prying woodwork loose. Some have checkered faces designed to reduce flying nails and glancing blows, but the most common head has a slightly crowned face with bevelled edges. It is tempered and should be used only to drive common nails, never hardened masonry nails or other tempered steel fasteners. Striking a hardened material may cause chips to break off the hammer head.

Ball peen hammers have rounded, slightly crowned striking faces with bevelled edges, and a ball-shaped peen at the other end. They are used for striking chisels and punches, for riveting, and for shaping, etc. A ball peen hammer should have a striking face that is at least 9 mm (3/8 in.) larger in diameter than the tool it strikes.

SAFETY SENSE

- Use each striking tool only for the purposes for which it was designed.
- Always grip the hammer near the end of the handle to provide maximum force to the blow.
- Swing the hammer handle so the face contacts the surface you are hitting squarely, not at an angle. If you find you are bending a lot of nails, check your swing to see if you're hitting the nail head on the side.
- Use only the face of a hammer for striking. Never strike with the side or

cheek of a hammer; these areas are not designed or tempered for striking.

- If a striking tool shows dents, cracks, chips, mushrooming or excessive wear, it is worn out and dangerous. Do not try to regrind it to shape; discard it!
- Never use a hammer with a loose handle; the head may fly off and cause serious injury.
- Replace or tighten loose handles with the proper wedges. Never use nails or staples for wedges. Steel or fibreglass handles are more difficult to repair than wooden ones. Some can be tightened with epoxy materials.
- Always wear safety glasses when using a hammer, especially if a ball peen hammer is striking another metal tool. Even a small fragment flying into your eye can blind you.

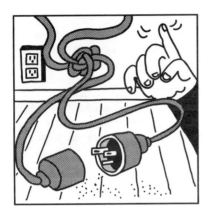

Basic Electrical Safety

RISK FACTORS

• Eleven percent of home deaths are a result of injury from electric current, explosive materials, hot substances, corrosive liquids, or steam.

CONTRIBUTING FACTORS

• frayed electrical cord
• cutting off electrical cord
• improperly grounded equipment
• overloaded circuits

COMMENT

Electrical extension cords and tool cords are adversely affected by moisture, oil, heat, and handling. If you notice any abrasion of the protective covering, replace the cord promptly. Ensure that all replacement and extension cords are correctly rated for the tools or loads they will be carrying.

SAFETY SENSE

• Inspect tools, power cords, and electrical fittings for damage before each use. Repair or replace damaged equipment.
• Switch tools off before connecting them to a power supply or making any adjustments.
• Ensure tools are properly grounded or double-insulated. A grounded tool must have an approved three-wire cord with a three-prong plug, which should be plugged into a properly- grounded three-hole outlet. Replace any broken or damaged plugs.
• Test tools for effective grounding with a continuity tester or a ground fault circuit interrupter (GFCI) before using them.
• Never bypass the switch and operate the tools by connecting and disconnecting the power cord.
• Do not use an electrical tool in wet conditions or damp locations unless it is connected to a GFCI.

• Do not clean tools with flammable or toxic solvents or operate tools in an area containing explosive vapors or gases.
• Do not carry electrical tools by their power cords or tie power cords in knots. This can cause short circuits and shocks.
• If any cord feels more than comfortably warm, have it checked by an electrician.
• Do not plug several power cords into one outlet.
• Disconnect the power supply by pulling on the plug, not by jerking the cord. Pulling the cord causes wear and may cause a shock.
• Use extension cords only temporarily to supply power to an area that does not have an electrical outlet.
• Do not allow vehicles to pass over unprotected power cords. Cords should be put in a conduit or protected by placing planks alongside them.

HOME CRAFTS

An art school student started having difficulty breathing, and developed headaches and sores in the lining of his nose. At first he thought his condition was a recurring cold, but when he realized that the symptoms only happened when he was painting, he sought advice from the school nurse. It turned out that he was having a reaction to turpentine and other solvents used in his artwork. When he stopped painting, the symptoms disappeared.

An amateur photographer who worked in her darkroom on weekends suddenly found she had red rashes all over her hands. Because she had no problems in the past, she didn't connect the symptoms with her hobby. Then she read about the hazards of darkroom chemicals in a photography magazine and realized the rashes might be linked to photographic developers. When she started using rubber gloves and tongs, the rashes disappeared.

People often do not realize they may be at risk from their hobbies. Yet anyone involved in arts and crafts risks exposure to substances that can cause health problems such as the ones in these two examples. Many commonly-used craft materials and processes are not as harmless as they seem. Whether you work with wood, glass, metal, clay, ink, or some other substance, you should be aware of the potential hazards and do what you can to reduce them. One important step is to get the facts about any chemicals you use in your craft work. Ask at your public library for reference works or craft guilds that give detailed information about such substances and their hazards.

NOTE: There is no statistical data available in North America which conclusively lists deaths attributed to home craft activities. However, there is a real danger associated with toxic art materials and long-term health. In 1981, the National Cancer Institute (USA), which surveyed 1,598 artists, reported that "artists who had a lifetime of exposure to pigments and solvents 'had significantly' elevated risks of contracting heart disease, leukemia, and cancers of the bladder, colon, rectum, kidney and brain." Persons interested in the health effects of different home craft materials and supplies should contact:

Center for Safety in the Arts
5 Beekman Street
New York, New York   10038
(212) 227-6220

The Center also publishes the Art Hazards News, a four-page newsletter which appears ten times per year and covers such topics as new hazards, precautions, etc. You can also contact:

Ontario Crafts Council
Resource Centre
346 Dundas Street West
Toronto, Ontario   M5T 1G5
(416) 977-3551

Some material in this unit is reproduced with permission of the Minister of Supply and Services Canada 1990.

Woodworking

RISK FACTORS
• No North American data available.

CONTRIBUTING FACTORS
• inhalation
• absorption
• lack of protective equipment and clothing
• fire
• poor ventilation of work areas
• allergic reactions to various woods
• noise
• machine vibration

COMMENT

Wood dusts, the most serious hazard in woodworking, are associated with a specific type of nasal and sinus cancer. Many wood dusts are toxic and can cause skin irritation, allergies, conjunctivitis, asthma, and serious lung damage. Rosewood, Canadian and western red cedar, cocobolo, mahogany, and satinwood are among the common offenders.

Particle board, plywood, preserved wood, wood preservatives, and other composite forms are also hazardous, especially during sawing or sanding, because of the formaldehyde glues and resins they contain. Formaldehyde can cause allergic reactions, irritation of the skin, eyes, and respiratory system, and is a suspected carcinogen.

Glues can be highly toxic and irritating when inhaled or brought into contact with skin. Among the most hazardous are formaldehyde-resin glues, which, when sanded after curing, may decompose into formaldehyde. Epoxy glues may cause allergic reactions and irritation to the skin, eyes, and respiratory system. Contact adhesives containing hexane are extremely flammable and can cause nerve damage. Those containing methylchloroform can, in large doses, provoke heart problems.

SAFETY SENSE

• Learn from local crafts guilds about the hazards of the materials and processes you use. Avoid glues containing formaldehyde and solvents wherever possible. Ensure

containers are well sealed when not in use.
• Never eat, drink, or smoke in the work area, and wash hands and arms thoroughly before eating or preparing

food.

- Wear special work clothes and wash them separately from other laundry.
- Wet-mop or wet-vacuum all surfaces daily; sweeping stirs up dusts.
- Equip all dust-producing machinery with efficient dust collectors. When working with particle board and plywood, exhaust formaldehyde-contaminated dusts to the outside.
- Use a respirator when working in heavy fine dust environments. Be sure it is approved by the National Institute of Occupational Safety and Health (NIOSH) for the particular substance you are using. For minimum protection, always wear a dust mask.
- Ensure good exhaust ventilation wherever glues and solvents are used.
- Wear eye protection and gloves when working with wood.

Glass Blowing and Stained Glass

RISK FACTORS
• No North American data available.

CONTRIBUTING FACTORS
• heat stress
• failure to wear eye protection
• carbon monoxide poisoning
• metal poisoning
• burns from acid, thermal and infrared sources

COMMENT

Many chemicals used to make glass are highly toxic, including lead, arsenic, and silica and its compounds. Furnaces for making glass present additional hazards, including poisonous carbon monoxide gas; infrared radiation, which can cause cataracts; and intense heat, which poses the risk of heatstroke.

When working freeblown glass, the risk of physical accidents is great as heavy gathers of glass are swung at the end of long pipes in an atmosphere of intense heat. This is also the most difficult stage at which to dispel the fumes, vapors, and toxic gases that form when colorants or other chemicals are added.

Coloring and decorating hazards depend on the processes and chemicals used. Fuming techniques, in particular, can create serious inhalation problems. Hydrofluoric acid and fluoride-salt etching can cause serious burns. Abrasive blasting with sand can produce silicosis, as well as hearing loss from noise.

When working with stained glass, lead is the most serious hazard; it can be inhaled or ingested while soldering, or sanding, and while applying lead-based pigments. Both lead-came and copper-foil techniques produce lead fumes, but copper-foil is more hazardous because higher temperatures are required.

Soldering fluxes produce fumes when heated. Many, such as zinc chloride, are severe lung irritants. Inhaling rosin fluxes can lead to asthma.

- Learn about the hazards of the materials and processes you use from a crafts guild.
- Never allow young children in the work area.
- Never eat, drink, or smoke in the work area. Wash hands and arms thoroughly before eating or preparing food.
- Wear special work clothes and wash them separately from other laundry.
- Wet-mop or wet-vacuum all surfaces daily; sweeping stirs up dusts.
- If you are pregnant, avoid using products containing lead or powdered pigments.
- If you have heart or kidney problems, check with your doctor before risking the high temperatures glass blowing requires.
- Wear protective equipment: infrared goggles and nonasbestos gloves when glass blowing; acid-proof goggles and clothing when etching; and hearing protectors for abrasive blasting, which, when done outside an enclosed cabinet, requires special respiratory protection.
- Use cullet or prepared glass whenever possible to avoid the chemical hazards of making glass.
- Use fluoride pastes instead of more hazardous hydrofluoric acid when etching.
- When blasting with abrasives, substitute glass beads, aluminum oxide, or silicon carbide (carborundum) for sand. For working indoors, enclosed blasting cabinets are essential.
- Ensure good ventilation. Gas-fired furnaces must be vented, preferably with a canopy hood. Solder stained glass directly in front of a window equipped with an exhaust fan, or use a slot hood. For etching and fuming, use a fume hood.
- Use a respirator as a last resort. Be sure it is approved by NIOSH for the substance you are using.

Metals

RISK FACTORS
• No North American data available.

CONTRIBUTING FACTORS
• exposure to infrared and ultraviolet radiation
• burns from molten metal, electric arc, or solder
• inhalation of metal fumes and gases
• electrical shock

COMMENT

Metal fumes from welding or other processes are a major hazard. Galvanized metals and zinc or copper alloys can induce the flu-like symptoms of metal-fume fever. Exposure to cadmium fumes can cause chemical pneumonia as well as lung and kidney damage.

Welding creates large amounts of infrared and ultraviolet light, which can cause skin cancer, severe sunburn, and eye damage.

Arc welding can produce nitrogen dioxide and ozone, both severe lung irritants that can cause immediate chemical pneumonia and long-term lung damage. The compressed gases used in oxyacetylene welding could cause fire and explosions. Other welding hazards include burns and electrical shock.

Metal hazards include the inhalation of dusts, fumes and gas, as well as heat, noise, and infrared radiation. For example, products used for molds can produce enough dust to cause silicosis. Resin-casting sands are usually based on formaldehyde, a highly toxic irritant of skin and the respiratory tract; lacquers, especially when sprayed, can induce acute narcosis and possible chronic damage to nerves, liver and kidneys; and buffing, polishing and grinding, in addition to obvious mechanical hazards, can produce particles and dusts hazardous to the eyes and respiratory system.

Soldering hazards include being burned from the heat or solder paste, which is an acid, and the potential of lead poisoning, which can cause damage to kidneys and lungs.

SAFETY SENSE

- Learn about the hazards of the materials and processes you use from a local crafts guild.
- Never allow young children in the work area.
- Never eat, drink, or smoke in the work area. Wash hands and arms thoroughly before eating or preparing food.
- Wear special work clothes and wash them separately from other laundry.
- If you are pregnant, avoid products containing lead, cadmium, or powdered pigments.
- If you have hearing or kidney problems, check with your doctor before risking the high temperatures of foundry work.
- Ensure good ventilation: canopy hoods for furnaces and kilns, and specialized exhaust systems (vented outside) for welding.
- Use a respirator as a last resort. Be sure it is approved by NIOSH for the substance you are using.
- Wear protective equipment: welding helmet, goggles, face shield, safety shoes, hearing protectors, and fire resistant, asbestos-free work clothes and gloves.
- Never use solvents in welding areas.

- Substitute Sparex for other acids. Always add acid to water, not vice versa. Wear acid-proof gloves and goggles.
- Maintain machinery and inspect it regularly for electrical hazards. Keep long hair, clothing, and jewelry away from machinery and torches.

When handling or storing fuel cylinders:
- Always double-check the contents of a new cylinder.
- Move cylinders in an upright position with caps on.
- Store cylinders securely, far from traffic, heat sources, and electric wires.
- Use cylinders in the order they are received from the supplier.
- When a cylinder runs out, close the valve and mark the cylinder as empty.
- Store full and empty cylinders of each type of gas separately.
- When finished working, close cylinder valves and put on valve protection caps. Release the pressure from regulators and hose lines before moving or storing the cylinders.

Clays, Plasters, Wax, Stone Carving and Plastics

RISK FACTORS
• No North American data available.

CONTRIBUTING FACTORS
• improper handling of raw materials
• inhalation of fumes and gases
• exposure to hazardous materials (pigments, varnishes, lacquers)

COMMENT

When working with clay, inhalation of dusts, powders, toxic gases, and fumes poses the major hazard. Cancer and asbestosis may result from inhaling talc found in many low-fire and slip-casting clays. Powdered clay can release large quantities of crystalline silica, which may cause silicosis.

The principal ingredient of plaster is calcium sulphate, a mild lung irritant which, along with other additives, may cause skin or respiratory problems. When used for hand or face molds, hardening plaster can also cause serious burns.

Overheating wax creates flammable vapors and strong lung irritants. Hydrocarbon solvents, such as carbon tetrachloride, are extremely hazardous and can be fatal.

Carving soft stones can present inhalation dust problems, particularly with soapstone (silica, asbestos) and sandstone (silica). Silica is also a problem when working with granite and many gemstones. Machine tools create more dust than hand tools, and increase the risk of flying particles. Pneumatic tools can cause hearing loss and "white fingers" -- a vibration-related numbness that can lead to permanent damage of the circulatory system.

Working with plastic resins is extremely hazardous. Polyester (fibreglass), epoxy, acrylic, polyurethane, amino and formaldehyde resins and their hardeners, catalysts, and other additives can cause severe problems with skin and respiration. Many are highly flammable. Heating, sawing, and sanding of finished plastics can cause them to decompose into toxic substances: for example, polyurethane forms hydrogen cyanide.

SAFETY SENSE

- Learn about the hazards of the materials and processes you use from a crafts guild.
- Avoid processes involving plastics or dusts when working with children.
- Never eat, drink, or smoke in the work area. Wash hands and arms thoroughly before eating or preparing food.
- Wear special work clothes and wash them separately from other laundry.
- Wet-mop or wet-vacuum all surfaces daily; sweeping stirs up dusts.
- If you are pregnant, avoid products containing plastic resins and solvents.
- Ensure good ventilation: canopy hoods for kilns and specialized local exhaust ventilation for plastic resins.
- Use a respirator as a last resort. Be sure that it is approved by NIOSH for the substance you are using.

- When working with stone, plaster, or clay, avoid asbestos-contaminated material.
- Never use an open flame to heat wax, and never overheat it. Use varsol or naphtha to replace carbon tetrachloride. Avoid chlorinated synthetic waxes.
- Use pneumatic and electric tools with portable dust collectors. Prevent "white fingers" by taking frequent work breaks, keeping hands warm, and using comfortable hand-grips. Isolate noisy compressors.
- Wear protective equipment, such as goggles and a face shield, face mask, eye and hearing protectors, and non-asbestos gloves.
- Maintain machinery and inspect it regularly for electrical hazards.
- Keep long hair, clothing, and jewelry away from moving parts.

Printing and Graphic Arts

RISK FACTORS
• No North American data available.

CONTRIBUTING FACTORS
• inhalation, absorbtion, and ingestion of acids, pigments, and solvents
• electrical shock and burns
• excessive noise

COMMENT

Working in the printing and graphic arts hobbies may not be the most dangerous activity in the world, it does involve many of the same hazards faced in heavy industry. The best way to avoid accidents and injuries in this or any hobby is to know what the hazards are and how to avoid them.

The major hazards in printing and graphic arts are: the use and storage of toxic chemicals and flammable materials; noise from machinery; handling materials; and electrical problems.

SAFETY SENSE

• Look up the specific health hazards of the materials you are using in a comprehensive reference work or contact your local crafts guild. Never work with a material if its composition is unknown.
• To keep down the level of dust and vapors in the air while you're working, keep all containers closed except when you're currently using them.
• Clean spills with materials that readily absorb the liquid, such as paper towels or terry cloths.
• Follow manufacturers' recommendations for disposing of waste material.
• Use gloves and barrier creams to protect your skin. Gloves must be approved for the type of chemical you're handling. Work with a face mask, and ensure that you have

good ventilation in the work area.
• Wear safety glasses when working with any material that could damage your eyes.
• Wash thoroughly after working with chemicals, paying close attention to cleaning your hands and fingernails.
• Never use solvents to clean any part of your body; they irritate the skin and can be absorbed into the bloodstream.
• Launder your work clothes frequently. Change your clothes immediately if you spill something on them.
• Never eat, drink, or smoke while working.
• Replace hazardous materials with safe ones which can be recommended by your crafts guild.

PROTECTING YOUR BODY

People frequently injure various parts of their bodies while using machines or other equipment, both on the job and at home. Statistics are available for many kinds of on-the-job injuries, and some large companies have estimated that approximately four times as many injuries occur off the job (in the home, at play, etc.).

Today, manufacturers are designing equipment with numerous guards and safety devices to help protect the operator and people close by. Often, the equipment will not operate unless these protective devices are in place. However, the safe operation of some machines requires that the operator wear protective clothing or equipment designed to prevent or minimize injury in case of accidents or to protect the wearer from environmental hazards.

Safety equipment exists to protect us from head to toe. However, each specific piece only offers protection under certain conditions, and, therefore, it is important to know what is available and understand how to use it. The most important thing to keep in mind about personal protective equipment is that it is only effective if it is used.

NOTE: There are no statistics available on household bodily injuries. The data used in this section comes from on-the-job national work injuries.

Eyes

RISK FACTORS
- Eye injuries account for five percent of all work-related body injuries.

CONTRIBUTING FACTORS
- foreign object striking the eye
- splash from a chemical or solvent
- direct exposure to the sun or other ultraviolet light

COMMENT

For most of us, sight is the most important of our senses. It is especially vital to avoid any risk of injury to our eyes. Remember that accidents can happen quickly, before our natural protective mechanisms have time to react.

Fortunately, most eye injuries are minor. They can be serious, however, and cause an enormous loss to the injured. Nearly all machine-related eye injuries can be avoided if operators wear approved protective equipment and follow sensible safety precautions.

SAFETY SENSE

- Use protective eyewear for any household tasks that pose the danger of eye injury. This includes trimming hedges, using hand or power tools, or cleaning with household chemicals.
- Inspect your safety glasses regularly and follow manufacturer's instructions for cleaning them. Handle them carefully when cleaning to avoid causing sight-impairing scratches and weakening the lenses.
- Store your glasses in a clean, dry place where they can't fall or be stepped on.
- Replace scratched, broken, bent, or ill-fitting eyewear immediately. Damaged eyewear interferes with your ability to see and is a hazard in itself.
- If you get anything in your eye (e.g.,
dirt, metal, eyelash), flush it with water until the object has been rinsed out. Don't rub your eye, since this may cause a scratch or imbed the object.
- If you are splashed by chemicals, go immediately to a shower or other water source and look directly into the stream of water, holding your eyes open with your fingers for at least 15 minutes. Get medical attention.
- Never attempt to remove embedded objects; get medical attention immediately.
- Be aware that light burns from welding or radiant light probably won't affect you until four to 12 hours later. If your eyes become irritated following such activity, seek medical attention.
- Supervise children using BB and air pellet guns.

Hands

RISK FACTORS
• Hand injuries account for five percent of all work accidents.

CONTRIBUTING FACTORS
• sharp edges on materials
• spinning and "in-running" pinches
• punctures
• crushing
• failure to use the correct hand protection

COMMENT

We use our hands so much, for so many different tasks, that they are particularly likely to be injured. For the same reasons, hand injuries are especially inconvenient, and it is worth a little extra attention to protect them.

Many machines commonly found in the home can seriously injure or even amputate a hand by shearing, smashing, rotating, puncturing, or pinching in an "in-running nip" -- (i.e., catching the skin between wheels, rollers, gears, or shafts that turn inward together). You should know the emergency shut-down procedures for any equipment/appliance you own, and be familiar with first aid techniques.

SAFETY SENSE

• Wear safety gloves designed for the job you are doing. Protection against different hazards (e.g., cuts, electrical shocks, chemicals, etc.) calls for different types of gloves.
• Use hand barrier creams when working with mildly irritating substances that do not require gloves. These creams can help prevent dermatitis and other skin problems.
• Take frequent rest breaks when working on intensive projects. Short-term overextension of the hand can cause injuries to the tendons, bones, muscles, and nerves of the hands and other joints.

• Remove rings when working with moving machinery/appliances.
• Avoid wearing loose clothing or dangling jewelry; it may get caught.
• Be sure your gloves are comfortable so you will not be tempted to take them off. Get the right size, and use cotton liners if necessary.
• Know when not to wear gloves. Some moving machinery/appliances can catch glove fabric and pull your hand in.
• Keep cutting tools sharp, and always cut away from your body.
• Do not use your bare hands for jobs that should be done with tools.

Feet

RISK FACTORS
- Foot injuries are the result of about six percent of all workplace accidents.

CONTRIBUTING FACTORS
- lack of proper footgear
- carelessness
- kicking at objects when upset
- walking in dark areas
- tripping
- over-confidence

COMMENT

Our feet are irreplaceable. They keep us upright, move us around, and support the weight of our bodies. Even our toes, which we often take for granted, are more important than most people realize; without a full set, walking and even standing become much more difficult. Fortunately, almost all injuries to feet and toes can be prevented by wearing appropriate and properly-maintained footgear in potentially hazardous situations.

The most common safety footwear is a shoe or a boot with a built-in steel toe cap to protect against dropped or falling objects. However, many other features are available in safety footwear. Various kinds of equipment protect against sole punctures, impact on the instep and ankles, burns, chemicals, electrical shock, heat, and cold.

Toe injuries are most often caused by falling objects. A direct blow to a toenail can be very painful, producing a collection of blood under the nail which may cause the nail to come off.

Injuries to the ankles are more often the result of a bend, twist, or tear. In serious cases, the ligaments are damaged, but even sprains are painful and slow to heal. Should an ankle fracture, the consequences can be extremely serious. The blood supply may be cut off to part of the bone which may cause the bone to die.

An injury to the instep of the foot can be very serious. Fractures of the bones in this area can lead to a permanent deformity.

Fractures to the heel bones are usually caused by falls from heights. This type of impact injury can seriously effect feet, but the damage to each foot may not be the same.

SAFETY SENSE

- When purchasing safety shoes, check with the sales department to ensure your footwear conforms to appropriate safety standards for the type of work you will be doing.
- Once you have your protective footgear, maintain it: clean it properly, and apply waterproofing or chemically resistant coating if necessary.
- Inspect your footwear regularly for signs of damage or wear, which can reduce its effectiveness. A stell cap won't protect your toes if it is exposed through worn leather or knocked out of place. Shock-resistant soles are ineffective if they get wet or contaminated by chemicals, such as road salt, or if a thumb tack gets stuck in the soles (it can conduct a shock right through the insulation).
- Choose shoes with comfortable low heels for everyday wear to help avoid twisted ankles, pinched toes, and tired feet.

Hearing

RISK FACTORS
- An estimated 15 million North Americans work at sites where the noise level presents an increased risk of hearing loss.

CONTRIBUTING FACTORS
- environmental noise in excess of 80-90 decibels
- failure to use ear protection
- failure to hear warnings resulting in accidents

COMMENT

Hearing is a delicate and complex process. Sound waves captured by our ears are transformed into nerve impulses and sent to the brain. Damage to any part of this system by exposing it to too much noise can affect hearing ability or even destroy it permanently.

Anybody exposed to high levels of noise for long periods of time can suffer noise-induced hearing loss. The amount of damage depends first of all on the amount of noise experienced -- both the intensity of the noise and the length of exposure. It also depends upon the susceptibility of the person involved; some people have more sensitive hearing than others.

The best way to safeguard your hearing is to wear protective equipment in any excessively noisy situations. These devices reduce the amount of noise reaching your ears. They also, of course, lower speech sounds, but may actually help you to understand what people are saying because there is less background noise and distortion.

SAFETY SENSE

- Always wear the correct hearing protection device for the specific conditions under which you work. Do not try to substitute one kind of device for another.
- Ensure that plugs, caps, and muffs are properly fitted and maintained to obtain maximum protection.

- Remember that the effects of noise can be cumulative and that early hearing loss may not be very noticeable. If you work under noisy conditions and detect even a slight problem with hearing, consult your doctor immediately.

Head

RISK FACTORS
- Six percent of all workplace accidents affect the head.

CONTRIBUTING FACTORS
- failure to wear head protection
- hair caught in machinery
- open cabinet doors
- bumping into things, e.g., low doorways, tree branches, etc.

COMMENT

Nature has provided good primary protection for your head -- and the delicate organ it contains, your brain -- in the form of a hard skull. It is not hard enough, however, to guard against all the dangers around us: falling objects, low beams and scaffolds, swinging planks and pipes, electrical circuits, corrosive liquids, etc. Because your brain is all-important, hazards that pose the risk of head injury are extremely serious and should be considered life-threatening. The best way to prevent head injury is to eliminate such hazards from the home or work environment as much as possible.

If the victim of a head injury is fortunate, she/he will receive only minor bumps or bruises. But whenever the head strikes or is struck by a hard object, there is the risk of brain damage or skull fracture -- or both, since they can occur in combination.

SAFETY SENSE

- Be sure your personal protective headwear has been approved by the Canadian Standards Association and/or National Institute of Occupational Health and Safety.
- Keep your protective headwear in good condition, and check it thoroughly for damage if it is dropped or hit.
- If using headwear accessories, such as earmuffs for hearing protection, chin straps, or winter liners, use only those designed for use with your protective headwear.

- Never substitute one kind of head protection for another. Nets designed to keep hair away from moving machine parts, for example, may provide some protection, but are not effective against impact injury and should never be used as a substitute for proper protective headwear.
- Never leave anyone with a serious head injury unattended. Be aware that a head injury victim may lose consciousness, have trouble breathing, or vomit (and possibly choke).

137

Respiratory

RISK FACTORS
- An estimated 1.5 out of every 10,000 full-time workers are treated for a respiratory condition caused by the work environment.

CONTRIBUTING FACTORS
- failure to use breathing apparatus when required
- inhalation of mist (suspended liquid droplets)
- inhalation of gases, smoke, dust, aerosols, fumes, and chemical products

COMMENT

Many substances found in our home, work, and leisure environments can release harmful gases, fumes, and mists into the air. Often times common activities, such as home renovations, repairs, maintenance, craft, and hobby work, will release these substances. Breathing this air can transfer these toxic materials into the body. They first enter the lungs and are then passed into the blood stream via the capillaries. These capillaries are extremely sensitive blood. They are vessels that are needed to transfer oxygen from our lungs to our blood. They are very delicate and can themselves be seriously damaged by toxic substances.

Besides harming the lungs, some gases and airborne contaminants can injure other parts of the body. For example, a significant concentration of ammonia vapor can cause skin burns, and certain acidic gases can penetrate the skin and directly poison the blood.

SAFETY SENSE

- Be sure there is an effective, well-designed ventilation system in operation whenever using processes or materials that may release toxic substances. This includes welding, foundry, forging, using acids, etc.
- Use the right respiratory protective equipment: for example, a filter mask to protect against brief exposure to dust, but a self-contained breathing apparatus for situations with a low level of oxygen in the air (below 19.5%).
- Be sure you fit your respirator using proper procedures, clean and inspect it after each use, and store it in an area that is convenient and sanitary.
- If someone shows symptoms of oxygen deficiency (face, lips, nail beds of fingers and toes may become blue), or of having inhaled a poisonous substance, get the victim and everyone else nearby to fresh air right away. If you suspect poisoning, call your local poison control center for treatment directions.
- If you must rescue someone from a dangerous area, wear protective equipment and make sure it's fitted correctly, or you may have to be rescued yourself.

Body

RISK FACTORS
• Nearly ten percent of workplace accidents lead to bodily injury.

CONTRIBUTING FACTORS
• failure to wear protective clothing
• failure to clean clothes of solvents and greases

COMMENT

Your body is vulnerable to injury and requires protection, perhaps even more so than the limbs, because it has a much larger surface area and only a soft layer protecting your internal organs. Protection is needed not only from physical forces, but also chemicals and environmental hazards, such as extreme temperatures.

SAFETY SENSE

• Avoid over-exposure to the sun. Working without a shirt on a hot sunny day may seem like a good idea, but may in fact lead to sunburn, sunstroke, or heat exhaustion. Discomfort from the sun also affects us emotionally; irritability and lack of concentration may lead to an injury.
• In cold weather, dress warmly enough to be comfortable, but beware of overheating.
• Before you undertake a job, find out what you will be working with so you can arrange for the right protection.
• Wear chemical-resistant aprons or garments when working with any substance that can cause irritation, such as solvents or dust. Ordinary clothing will absorb chemicals and prolong exposure.

• When handling highly hazardous substances (such as anhydrous ammonia, which will freeze and dehydrate human flesh on contact), wear a full impervious suit.
• When wearing protective clothing:
  - keep shirts and jackets zipped or buttoned; there is less chance of entanglement.
  - avoid wearing loose clothes; well-fitted clothes which offer freedom of movement are best.
  - do not wear dangling earrings, necklaces, or scarves. They can get caught in a machine or power tool.
• Keep your work clothes clean. Clothing soaked with grease, oil or solvents can give you a skin rash or a disabling case of dermatitis.

EMERGENCY PREPAREDNESS

Have you ever wondered what you would do if your community were struck by a natural disaster, such as an earthquake, tornado, or hurricane? Even a heavy rainstorm or snow blizzard can damage property and endanger lives. You should know what you can do to protect your family and your home in such an emergency. Disasters strike quickly -- some things cannot be left until warnings are issued. You should think about them now.

- The first step is to be informed. Know what types of storms could occur in your area and at what time of year they are likely to strike.

- Is your area flood-prone, or on a fault line where earthquakes are common? The broadcast media provide weather warnings; if you listen, you will usually have some advance notice of bad storms.

- Prepare an emergency pack. This should include an emergency food supply as well as extra clothing, blankets, medication, and a first-aid kit. Include a battery-powered radio and spare batteries, too -- it might be your only link with the outside world. You might want to include tools (for making emergency repairs) and flashlights, lanterns, or other emergency lighting. Think about acquiring an alternate heat source in case of power failure during cold weather.

- Choose your shelter. Your basement, a storm cellar or fallout shelter, or a spot beneath stairs or underneath sturdy furniture on the ground floor are good places to weather storms. In a storm or earthquake, stay in the center of the building away from walls and windows. If you are planning home improvements, you might want to consider strengthening an interior room against storm winds.

- Reduce the hazards. Trim dead or rotting branches and cut down dead trees to reduce the danger of limbs falling on your home. Check the landscaping; be careful of the drainage around your home. If you live in an earthquake area, bolt down gas appliances, and avoid storing heavy items high up. If you store valuable items in the basement, be sure they can be moved easily in case of flooding.

- Ensure that responsible members of your family know first-aid techniques. Hospitals and clinics may be overloaded after a severe earthquake.

- Teach your family how to turn off electricity at the main switch and gas and water at the main valves.

Special thanks goes to Emergency Preparedness Canada for permission to use selected material from their "Self-help Advice" brochure for inclusion in this unit.

- Hold occasional home emergency drills to be sure your family knows what to do under different kinds of emergencies.

- In new construction and alterations, select building sites and follow building codes to minimize earthquake hazards.

- Bolt down or provide other strong support for water heaters and gas appliances, since fires can result from broken gas lines and appliance connections. Use flexible connections wherever possible. Place large and heavy objects on lower shelves of cupboards, bookcases, etc.

- Choose a meeting place. If disaster strikes, you might be separated from members of your family who are at home, work, or school. Avoid unnecessary worry and travel by arranging now to have a family meeting place or system of communication after an emergency to ensure no one is lost or in need of help.

- Ensure mobility afterwards. Keep a fairly full tank of gasoline in your car, since filling station pumps may not operate for several days after a disaster.

Earthquakes

RISK FACTORS
- Since earthquakes are only a problem in certain key geographical areas, your chance of accidental injury as a result of an earthquake depends largely on where you live. On average, however, some 40 people die annually in North America in earthquakes or as a result of the destruction they cause.

CONTRIBUTING FACTORS
- crushed by falling objects
- struck by flying objects
- failure to follow emergency procedures at the onset of a quake

COMMENT

The actual movement of the ground in an earthquake is seldom the direct cause of death or injury. Most casualties result from falling objects and debris because the quake and aftershocks (which may follow hours or days later) damage or demolish buildings and other structures. Earthquakes can also trigger landslides and generate huge ocean waves (called tsunamis or seismic sea waves).

Buildings do not automatically collapse in earthquakes. Some, such as timber-frame houses, may withstand shock very well. Even if the structure stands, however, chimneys, parapets, ceiling plaster and light fixtures may fall. There could be flying glass from broken windows. Fires may break out due to broken chimneys and gas lines, and the danger aggravated by broken water mains. Fallen power lines are another hazard, and could leave communities without power for days.

SAFETY SENSE

During an Earthquake:
- Stay calm. Don't panic.
- If you are indoors, stay there. Outside, you might be hit by falling debris. If you are in a house, store, or highrise building, take cover under heavy furniture and hold onto it. If it moves, move with it. Stay away from windows. If you are unable to get under a piece of furniture, flatten yourself against an interior wall. (The inner core of a building is its strongest point and least likely to collapse.) Do not dash for exits, as stairways may be broken and jammed with people. Do not use elevators as power may fail.
- If you are outside, stay there. Move away from buildings to avoid crumbling walls and falling debris. Stay away from power lines and dangling electric wires.
- If you are driving, stop quickly, but stay in your car. Avoid stopping on a

bridge or overpass, or where buildings can fall on you.

After an earthquake
- Listen to your battery-operated or car radio for instructions. Follow them.
- Check for fires. In case of fire, notify the fire department. Try to control small fires until help arrives.
- Give first aid to injured persons; get help if necessary. Help others who may be trapped by debris. Exercise caution; do not injure yourself.
- Do not re-enter damaged buildings. Walls may collapse after the original shaking has ceased.
- Check all utilities for broken water pipes, shorting electrical circuits, or leaking heating fuel. Do not use a match or open flame to find your way.
- If you find or suspect damage, shut off utilities at main valves or meter boxes. Turn off heating appliances and check for damage.
- Do not use the telephone except in a real emergency. Leave the lines open for official use.
- If water is off, use emergency water from water heaters, toilet tanks, melted ice cubes and canned vegetables.
- Check that sewage lines are intact before flushing toilets.
- If power is off, use food from the freezer before it spoils. Use outdoor charcoal or gas barbecues for emergency cooking.
- Check chimneys for cracks, particularly in the attic and the roof line. Unnoticed damage can lead to fire.
- Do not go sightseeing. Drive your car only if necessary, and then with caution. Keep the roads clear for rescue and emergency vehicles. Do not enter damaged areas unless you have been asked by officials to do so.
- Keep your emergency supplies, clothing and food handy in case you are called on to evacuate. You will be advised if it becomes necessary to evacuate your home.
- Wear shoes to protect your feet from debris or broken glass.
- Stay away from waterfront areas. Large earthquakes at sea are often followed by tidal waves.

Winter Power Failures

RISK FACTORS
• No North American data available.

CONTRIBUTING FACTORS
• extreme exposure to cold
• lack of emergency supplies, especially in rural areas

COMMENT

Most North American home-heating systems are dependent upon electric power to operate furnace, forced-air circulation, and thermostat controls. Power supply interruptions can last from a few hours to several days, and are often caused by freezing rain or sleet storms which damage power lines and equipment. An extended power failure during winter months and subsequent loss of heating can result in cold, damp homes, severe living conditions, and damage to walls, floors, and plumbing.

You can reduce the consequences of cold-weather power and heating failure in two ways: by having an emergency standby heating system, which will permit continued occupancy throughout the emergency or, should you be forced to leave the house temporarily because of cold, by protecting it against frost damage before you go.

SAFETY SENSE

Advance precautions
• If you have a fireplace, keep a good supply of fuel on hand.
• Install a standby stove or heater which does not require electricity. If required, make sure it is vented (one way of doing this is by connecting it to an unused flue). Use only certified fuel-burning heaters.
• If the standby heating unit will use the normal house oil or gas supply, have it connected with shut-off valves by a competent technician from the fuel supplier.
• Have flashlights, lanterns, candles, and matches or other emergency lighting devices stored in a handy place.
• Check with your local supply authority before arranging for installation of emergency generators for furnaces, appliances, or lighting.
• Have a battery-powered radio, with

spare batteries, to keep you informed; many broadcast stations can
operate using emergency power.

If there is power failure

• Check to see whether your home is
the only one affected; if so, notify
your local electric supply authority.
• Don't panic. Even in very cold
weather, a house with doors and
windows closed will not become too
cold for comfort for several hours.
• If you have a standby heating unit,
turn it on before the house gets too
cold. If the unit must be vented to
the same chimney flue as the furnace, switch the furnace off before
disconnecting the furnace flue.
Check to see that no part of the
plumbing system can freeze.
• If all or part of the house must be
abandoned, protect it by taking the
following precautions:
  - turn off the main electric switch.
  - turn off the water main where it

enters the house. Protect valve,
inlet pipe, and meter or pump with
blankets or insulation material.
- open all water taps in the house,
including the drain on the water
heater, and flush toilets several
times to prevent freeze up if power
failure extends for lengthy period of
time.
- check the operating manuals of
your dishwasher, washing machine,
etc., for draining or frost protection
instructions.
- if you have horizontal water supply
lines which might not drain when
valves are open then blow out the
water with a tire pump.
• If the power failure has been lengthy,
check food supplies in refrigerators,
freezers and cupboards for signs of
spoilage. If a freezer door has been
kept closed food should stay frozen
for 24 to 48 hours.

Lightning

RISK FACTORS

• Nearly 100 people die in North America every year as the result of being hit by lightning.

CONTRIBUTING FACTORS

• failure to take safety precautions during storms
• standing near a window or a door
• talking on the telephone; watching television during the storm

COMMENT

Lightning is an electrical discharge resulting from the buildup of static electricity between two clouds or between clouds and the ground. It is present in all thunderstorms, more frequently in severe ones. More people are killed by lightning each year than by the other effects of violent storms.

You can estimate the distance of a lighting stroke by counting the seconds between the flash and thunderclap. Each second indicates about 300 m (1000 ft.). If you count fewer than five seconds, the lightning is near enough to cause concern.

SAFETY SENSE

• Stay indoors when there is lightning. Don't go outside unless absolutely necessary.
• If you are indoors, keep away from windows, doors, fireplaces, radiators, stoves, metal pipes, sinks, or other charge conductors. Disconnect electrical appliances, such as televisions and radios. Don't handle electrical equipment or telephones during a storm.
• If you are caught outdoors, seek shelter in a building, a cave, or an area lower than ground level (ditch etc.). Don't be the tallest object in an open area.
• If you are swimming or in a small boat, get back to shore and out of the water immediately.
• Keep away from fences and tele-

phone or power lines.
• Get off and away from equipment such as tractors, golf carts, motorcycles, lawnmowers or bicycles. They can be electrical conductors.
• Don't use metal shovels, golf clubs, clotheslines, etc.; anything long and metallic may conduct lightning to you.
• If you're caught in the open, kneel with your feet close together and lower your head. This makes you a smaller target, than if you lie flat.
• If you are in your car, stay there. It will give excellent protection from lightning. Pull away from trees that might fall, and wait until the storm passes and it is safe to drive again.
• If you are on a farm, try to get livestock to shelter.

Tornadoes

RISK FACTORS
- Death from tornadoes accounts for 12 percent of fatalities related to storms.

CONTRIBUTING FACTORS
- flying material
- failure to follow emergency procedures

COMMENT

Tornadoes or "twisters" are violent windstorms characterized by a twisting, funnel-shaped cloud which forms at the base of a cloud bank and points toward the ground. Tornadoes occur in conjunction with severe thunderstorms, and are accompanied by lightning and sometimes heavy rain or hail. Their destructive force comes from the extremely high winds -- 150 km/h (95 mph) and higher -- and very low air pressure which form a tornado.

Tornadoes strike suddenly; their loud roaring noise will alert you that one is coming. They move rapidly and normally touch ground for less than 20 minutes. Tornadoes usually occur between April and October (June and July are the peak months). If you live in a known tornado area, keep a battery-operated radio playing during thunderstorms and listen for severe weather warnings.

SAFETY SENSE

- Choose a shelter area in advance. If you spot a tornado, you probably won't have time to look for shelter. Know the best shelter space in your office, school, or place of work, as well as in your home. If you don't have a basement, an inner hallway or small inner room away from windows makes a good shelter. Mobile homes and cars offer no protection against the power of a tornado. It is far better to seek shelter elsewhere, preferably below ground. If no such shelter is available, then get as close to the ground as you can. Outside, lie down in a ditch, depression or culvert or hold on to a tree or bush. Inside, crouch or lie flat on the floor underneath heavy furniture. Protect your head with your hands.
- Hold tornado drills in your home and office during tornado season.
- Avoid large halls, cafeterias, arenas, etc.; their roofs are more likely to collapse.

Hurricanes

RISK FACTORS
- Two percent of all storm deaths can be attributed to hurricanes.

CONTRIBUTING FACTORS
- drowning
- being struck by flying objects
- failure to take safety precautions

COMMENT

Hurricanes are violent tropical storms which reach eastern North America from June to November, with September the peak month; they rarely occur on the Pacific coast. They cause more widespread damage than tornadoes. The outer edges of a hurricane have gusting winds up to 30 km/h (18 mph), increasing to gale force winds of 120 km/h (75 mph) and above towards the center. The actual center -- or "eye" -- of the storm is calm, and winds on the opposite side of it blow in the opposite direction.

Hurricanes are slow-moving; communities may be battered for several hours. High winds and torrential rains cause widespread damage and flooding; on coasts, hurricanes create huge waves or storm surges. Most people killed in hurricanes are caught in these floodwaters. If you live in a coastal or low-lying area, seek higher ground when a hurricane approaches.

SAFETY SENSE

During a hurricane:
- Keep the radio or television tuned to weather alerts.
- If there is a sudden lull in the wind, stay in a safe place. The "eye" of the storm is passing over, and it may last from a few minutes to half an hour or more.
- Make emergency repairs only if necessary, and remember that the wind will return suddenly from the opposite direction, with probably even greater force.
- If you are a mobile home owner, take these precautions to protect yourself and your property:
  - position your trailer near a natural windbreak, such as a hill or clump of trees. The narrow end should face in a westerly direction to make a smaller target for approaching storm winds.
  - make sure your trailer is securely anchored. Consult the manufacturer for information on secure tiedown systems.
  - even if your trailer is reasonably protected, when a severe storm is approaching, seek more permanent shelter. Trailers are the exception to the "stay indoors" rule.
- After a hurricane, stay away from the disaster area and let rescue people do their work.

Snow Blizzards

RISK FACTORS
- Five percent of all storms deaths are related to snow blizzards.

CONTRIBUTING FACTORS
- failure to take safety precautions during snow storms

COMMENT

Treat these severe winter storms with respect. Their high winds, extremely low temperatures, and heavy snowfall can endanger lives in minutes.

SAFETY SENSE

- If blizzard or heavy snowsquall warnings are broadcast several days beforehand, lay in a supply of heating fuel. Home delivery vehicles may not be able to get through during the storm.
- Ensure farm animals are stabled and have plenty of food and water before a storm.
- Do not go outdoors during a blizzard. In rural areas, if you cannot avoid travel between your house and outbuildings, tie one end of a rope securely to a doorknob or other marker at each building you must visit, starting with your house. Do this even if you are on familiar ground. Hold tightly to this lifeline when you are walking. Blowing snow can blind you and make you lose your way.
- Be prepared to wait out the storm indoors. Blizzards often last for days.
- Keep your radio tuned to a local station for weather advice.
- Carry an emergency storm kit in your car with supplies, such as candles, blankets, tow chain, food packs, etc.
- Know how to react if trapped in your car when a winter storm strikes:
  - drive with caution and measure your speed to conditions. Be defensive.
  - don't press on. If the going gets tough, turn back or seek refuge.
  - try to keep to main roads.

149

Floods

RISK FACTORS
• Floods account for thirteen percent of all fatalities related to storms.

CONTRIBUTING FACTORS
• sudden downpour of rain
• broken or washed-out dam

COMMENT

Floods occur in almost every part of North America and can result from any one of several factors: abnormally heavy rainfall, rising temperatures that melt snow rapidly, ice jams that block the flow of a river, or dam failure. Flash floods can occur with little or no warning, and are especially dangerous because their swift, debris-laden currents can strike suddenly with crushing force. In periods of heavy rain, flash floods may occur in urban areas where buildings and roads have been constructed on the flood plain. But most flash floods occur in mountainous regions, sometimes in popular camping areas.

SAFETY SENSE

• If you live in a flood-prone area, know the elevation of your property in relation to nearby bodies of water. Plan in advance how to quickly get to higher ground.
• If conditions dictate, i.e., forecast is for continued rain and rising water levels, turn off gas, electricity, and water before leaving your home.
• Leave immediately if a flash flood warning is issued for your area.
• As you head for higher ground, stay tuned to the radio and avoid flooded areas.
• If trapped at home by rising water, go to the second story if there is one, or even the roof, where there's a better chance of being spotted and rescued.
• Follow the instructions of local authorities to the letter, even if you can't perceive any threat.
• Never try to drive through water of unknown depth or walk through water higher than knee-level.
• If your vehicle stalls, abandon it immediately and climb to higher ground.
• Never enter a flooded basement when the water is high enough to have reached appliance motors or electrical equipment; call the electrical company and wait for them to shut off the power in the basement. (When under water, plugged-in electrical equipment and the wiring system itself can give off a fatal current. The current will travel through water seeking the nearest ground -- and you may be in its path).

PERSONAL SECURITY

Residents need to take special care in protecting themselves from crime and vandalism. The highest incidence of crime occurs inside high-rise apartments, particularly in public spaces, such as entrance lobbies, elevators, staircases, corridors, and parking garages. A great deal of crime also occurs outside in the public spaces surrounding these buildings, which are often not patrolled or controlled in any way.

The safest housing areas are those having a high degree of individual identification and control of outside space in the form of private patios and rear yards. Housing forms that provide individual identification and personal control over the environment are preferable to those with limited personal input and large areas of common space over which the individual has little control.

It is important that outside areas be specifically identified with individual dwelling units or small groups of dwelling units. This may be accomplished through the use of fences, porches, and landscaping. By clearly defining the outside space, residents will be able to readily identify non-residents -- those who do not have legitimate business in the neighbourhood.

Entrances should face the street and be easily approached. If pedestrians must pass through an area where they cannot be seen in order to reach their front door, this can be very dangerous.

All walkways and common areas should be open and well lit. Heavy planting in these areas should be avoided.

Underground parking areas require special consideration. The entrances to parking garages should have doors that can be opened only by an occupant's key or card. This should discourage intruders and vandals. In large apartment buildings, underground parking areas should be patrolled regularly and outfitted with a telephone.

Inside the apartment building, access by non-residents should be possible only after visitors have identified themselves to an occupant through the intercom system. Lobbies and corridors should be open and well lit, and elevators should have a telephone. Laundry rooms and recreation rooms should be locked and accessible only by tenants' keys.

These measures should discourage unauthorized intruders. The best deterrent, however, is to ensure that the occupants themselves are educated and aware of the dangers. Occupants should be encouraged to question and report any anti-social behavior.

Safety in Public Places

RISK FACTORS

• An estimated 85 percent of all violent crimes reported in North America are assaults. The second most frequent violent crime is robbery.

CONTRIBUTING FACTORS

• assaults, including sexual assault
• robbery
• attempted murder
• homicide
• abduction

COMMENT

Crimes of violence, like robbery, rape, and assault, are the most difficult crimes to prevent because they are often committed on impulse. The offender is frequently highly emotional and may be difficult to discourage. The best prevention is precaution -- be aware of your surroundings and alert to a situation that might develop into a violent one.

SAFETY SENSE

Purses, wallets, and handbags

• Prevent the loss of your purse by carrying it only when necessary; a wallet or billfold that fits in your pocket is much safer.
• When you must carry a purse, carry it close to your body and hang on tightly to it, especially in large crowds, where the possibility of purse snatching is greater.
• Do not wrap purse straps around your wrist -- you may be injured if your purse is snatched.
• Don't leave a purse or handbag unattended, even for a moment.
• Carry only what you need in a purse or wallet.
• Don't hesitate to ask for help if someone appears to be watching you

while you are at a bank or a store. If someone is threatening you, or if someone has stolen your purse or wallet, sound an alarm by shouting "police!" and by blowing a whistle, if you are carrying one. Don't hesitate to knock on a strange door or flag a passing motorist if you are outdoors.
• Keep a reserve of credit cards and money in a hotel or motel safe when you are travelling.
• Place bags and luggage in front of your seat where you can see them when travelling on planes, buses, trains, etc.
• Don't take anything of value to the beach if you have to leave it unattended while you are in the water.
• Be aware of people who may be

watching you when making withdrawals from an automatic banking machine, especially outside of normal banking hours.

Robbery

• As a general practice, do not carry valuable items or large sums of cash with you.
• Don't open your door to strangers during the day or at night unless you can verify why they are there. If they say it is an emergency, like an auto accident, make sure you heard it or can see it. You can talk to them through a closed door (especially if you install a peephole viewer) and offer to call a tow truck, the police, or anyone else they wish.
• Trust your instincts -- if you feel at all unsafe, take precautions immediately -- blow on a whistle; and shout "police" to alert people near you.
• Think ahead -- have your keys ready ahead of time when returning home at night. You won't have to stand at your front door fumbling for them.
• Always check the back seat of your car before getting into it to make sure no one is hiding there.
• Drive with doors locked and windows closed.
• If you are attacked by a robber, don't resist. This may prevent you from being assaulted. The introduction of automatic banking machines, many of them in 24-hour use, has created an additional opportunity for robbery to occur.
• Avoid making deposits at night, and never do it alone. When you can't avoid it, stagger your deposit hours so that a routine or pattern is not established. Always be aware of who may be watching you.
• Leave the area immediately and notify the police if you are at all suspicious.

Rape

• The precautions listed above for robbery can help you avoid being raped. Be defensive -- learn to avoid situations that could lead to a rape attempt. The question of whether to resist a person who is threatening to rape you is a complex one. A rapist with a weapon may use it if you resist. On the other hand, yelling loudly for help may be enough to deter the attacker. All women and girls should take a self-defence course that is designed specifically to teach them ways to deal with the threat of rape.
• Do not put your full first name on your mail box or in your telephone listing -- use your initial.
• Install and use a peephole viewer in the door of your home so that you can see who is outside. If you live alone, never let a stranger in, especially at night.
• Be aware that many rapes are committed by attackers known by the victim, not by strangers. If you feel threatened by a person you know, get out of the situation immediately and find help. If this means leaving your own home, do it.
• Be aware that many rapes occur after encounters on the street, at taverns, parties, or in parks. Giving and accepting rides can be very dangerous. The majority of rapes occur late at night, early in the morning, and on weekends.
• If you have been the victim of a rape, report the incident to the police immediately. Do not bathe or change clothes. Seek out the rape crisis center in your community -- it offers counselling and support to victims of this crime.

Assault

• Be aware that both offenders and victims involved in assault are more likely to be friends, relatives, or acquaintances, rather than strangers.

- Try to identify trouble ahead of time and avoid it if possible. This is not always easy, however. If your domestic situation has a continuing potential for assault, for example, you should seek professional counselling.

Crisis Situations

- Call a crisis intervention service if you are severely depressed, suicidal, or are in some other life-threatening situation. The friends and relatives of people needing help may also call. A battered woman or abused child who does not want to call the police should call a crisis assistance agency for help.

Preventing Child Abductions

RISK FACTORS
• Nearly 40 percent of all abductions in North America involve children under 16 years of age.

CONTRIBUTING FACTORS
• kidnapping by parents
• sexual assault by strangers

COMMENT

Millions of children under 18 are reported missing every year. Some are runaways, some are caught in the middle of custody disputes. Although many are found within hours of being reported missing, some simply disappear. Because no single agency keeps track of these reports, it is impossible to tell how many children are kidnapped. In each case, however, there is a frightened child and a grieving family. You should consider personal safety instruction just as important to your children as fire safety, water safety, traffic safety, or any of the other environmental hazards you teach them.

SAFETY SENSE

• Walk through the neighborhood with your children, and point out the safe places to play (a park or a friend's yard), as well as the unsafe places (alleys and deserted buildings). Discuss with your children where they should go if someone is following them -- perhaps a trusted neighbor's house or the nearest store or gas station.
• Consider using secret code words as a signal to your child that it's all right for them to go with an unfamiliar adult in an emergency. The code word can be a nonsense word or a pet's name that you and the child decide

to use in such situations. The unknown adult must volunteer the code word before the child agrees to go with him or her. Emphasize to the child, however, that the adult must mention the code word first.
• Ensure that your children know their full names, their parents' full names, their home address, telephone number and area code, and their state or province.
• Have your children practice making long distance telephone calls.
• Teach your children self-defence techniques that will take their attacker by surprise. Biting, stomping on the

foot, kicking the shins, and yelling for help are all good things to do.

- Instruct your child never to tell anyone on the phone or at the door that she/he is home alone.
- Never leave your child alone in the car.
- Encourage your child to have a friend with him/her at play, on errands, and on the way to and from school.
- Be sure your child's school will not allow him/her to go with any other adult unless they check first with you. Ensure that the school will contact you if your child doesn't show up in the morning.
- Keep current photos of your child -- have one taken at least every year, more often for preschoolers.
- Have your child fingerprinted if your community has such a program.
- Set up an after-school telephone check-in procedure with your child if she/he goes home to an empty house. Use a similar procedure when your child goes to a friend's house.
- Don't let your child wear clothes with her/his name on them; children will respond to someone who calls them by name.
- Teach your child to tell you, a teacher, or a neighbor immediately if anyone suspicious approaches them.
- Never let your child go to a public restroom alone.
- Find out if your police department, church, or school sponsors programs on street-proofing. If not, suggest that one of these groups set up such a program.
- Start a Block Parent Program in your community, and instruct children that they can go to Block Parent homes if they are in trouble or in need of assistance.

Babysitting

RISK FACTORS
• No North American data available.

CONTRIBUTING FACTORS
• failure to explain all security measures in the home

COMMENT

Children and parents need time apart once in awhile, hence the need for an occasional babysitter. When choosing a sitter, talk to neighbors about those available in your neighborhood. Learn about them and how they have performed their tasks for others. It is recommended that you choose a babysitter who has completed a babysitter training course, often approved by local safety councils, community recreation departments, the Red Cross, and church groups.

SAFETY SENSE

Safety Tips for Parents:
• Take the babysitter on a tour of the home and yard, pointing out any areas that are off-limits or dangerous to the child and showing the location of emergency exits.
• Show the babysitter how to change an electrical fuse, how to use a fire extinguisher, and the location of the first-aid kit.
• Provide a list showing the amounts to be taken and the time schedule for such items as medications, etc.
• Leave all necessary telephone numbers for the babysitter, such as doctor, neighbours, and, if possible, where the parents can be reached.
• Give the names and phone numbers of persons (neighbors) in the immediate area who will help if the need arises.
• If possible, call home during your absence.
• Babysitters should not accept a ride home from an intoxicated employer.

Safety Tips for Babysitters:
• Be sure you are physically and mentally prepared to babysit.
• Do not sleep. Stay awake on the job unless permission by parents has been given.
• Do not listen to music or television using earphones or other devices that may prevent you from hearing a child cry out or call your name.

- Never use drugs or alcohol while babysitting.
- Be sure to obtain emergency phone numbers, names, and information from parents.
- Follow parents' instructions.
- Observe any house rules given to you by parents regarding smoking, playing loud music, use of their appliances, etc.
- Keep doors and windows locked, and do not open the door to strangers.
- Stay alert, check children frequently during their sleep.
- If you suspect an intruder is trying to enter the house, call the police immediately. Do not investigate strange noises outside.
- Hang up immediately on unwelcome phone calls. If a second call occurs, call the parents or a neighbor as soon as the line is clear. Do not attempt to make conversation with such callers, and do not let them know you are babysitting alone.
- In answer to calls for the parents, respond with: "They are unable to come to the phone. May I take a message?" Do not give out any information unless instructed by the parents to do so.
- If a child who has been at a friend's house or at school does not return at the proper time, telephone the playmate or the school. If the child has left, and there is a time lapse, contact the parents and inform them. It should be the parents' decision, if they can be reached, to call the police. If the parents cannot be reached, contact a reliable adult.

Home Security

RISK FACTORS

- Break and enter into residences accounts for over 60 percent of all break and enter offenses in North America.

CONTRIBUTING FACTORS

- failure to secure home premises
- failure to notify neighbors of a prolonged absence from the home
- inadequate lighting from the home to the street area

COMMENT

The security of every home can be improved in order to frustrate or discourage a break-in attempt. Burglars usually look for an unoccupied residence so they can minimize their chances of being interrupted. This also reduces the threat of a violent reaction from the occupants, which could turn a break and enter into a more serious crime.

Unoccupied premises announce themselves in a variety of ways -- a completely dark house, a full mailbox, uncollected newspapers, an unanswered telephone, an empty garage, or a note indicating when the occupant will return. Read the following safety sense tips and avoid invitations to burglary.

SAFETY SENSE

- Ensure that your locks are properly installed, are of good quality, and that they have dead bolts. Use wraparound strike plates installed with 7.5 cm (3 in.) screws. This will add strength to the lock and prevent the door frame from splintering.
- Mount doors so that hinge bolts are not exposed on the outside. Hinges with pins that are easily removed can be a means of criminal entrance or exit. Avoid this possibility by installing a small set screw in each pin to hold it firmly in the hinge.
- Ensure that outside doors are of solid construction. Install a door viewer so you can see who is at the door before opening it.
- Reinforce all exterior door frames -- even the best locks and doors can be defeated by a burglary method known as "spreading".
- With sliding glass doors or windows, place a square-edged length of wood in the bottom track to prevent them from being forced open. To prevent the door from being lifted out of its track, install screws in the upper track, allowing just enough clearance for the door to slide. Door windows and basement windows should be made of break-resistant glass or acrylics.
- Know where all the keys for your

locks are located and never hide them on door ledges, under door mats, or in mail boxes. These are the first places experienced thieves look.

• Have the locks changed immediately if you have lost or mislaid your keys.

• Ensure that window locks are in good working condition and that you use them.

• Increase your security by installing key-operated window locks in windows that provide easy access to your home. Be aware, however, that these windows may not be used to escape in an emergency.

• Pin your windows for security purposes. Drill a 4.8 mm (3/16" in.) hole on a slight downward slant through the inside window frame. A nail or pin can then be placed in the hole to secure the window.

• Be aware that ladders, garbage pails, trellises, and low roofs can be used by burglars to reach windows and doors.

• Check other access points to your home, such as air conditioning units and exhaust fans. Some older residences may still have milk, coal, and wood chutes that require special attention.

• Keep exterior lighting on from dust to dawn.

• Keep your garage locked to prevent access through it, and also to discourage burglars from using your tools to break into your home.

• Leave a light on in one or two rooms when you go out for the evening. You may also consider leaving a radio playing.

• When going away for extended periods, ask a neighbor to watch your home and notify police if they notice anything suspicious. Have all deliveries stopped. Have the neighbor pick up handbills and circulars regularly. Someone should shovel your sidewalk in winter and mow your lawn in summer, and you should have an automatic timing device turn your lights on and off at designated times.

• Keep your valuable possessions, such as expensive jewelry, stocks, and bonds, in a safety deposit box at your bank or trust company.

• Use an engraving tool or invisible ink pen to mark driver's license or social insurance numbers on all valued items.

• Keep a record of serial numbers and identifying marks on your valuables, including home furniture and appliances. Consult your insurance agent and local police department if you require further assistance in identifying your valuables.

• Invest in an alarm system for your home. Shop around to find the one best suited to your needs and pocket book. There are systems that are triggered by the sound of breaking glass, and others that sound a bell, buzzer, horn, or whistle. There are even some alarm systems that turn on lights.

• Keep shrubbery around the house well trimmed and away from doorways to prevent people from hiding behind them.

• Avoid vandalism by maintaining good security, keeping property well lit, and watching over it. Like robbery, most vandalism occurs where there is relatively easy opportunity to do damage without being caught.

• Form a Neighbourhood Watch Program. Contact your police department to find out how.

CHILD SAFETY

The most tragic accidental deaths and injuries in the world are those that happen to children. In this age of vast scientific and medical achievements, the greatest threat to children is still the accident. Accidents, not diseases, are the major cause of death to children one year old and over. Another tragic fact is that nearly all of these deaths could have been prevented by parents or guardians.

The years from birth to five are when children need the most protection from accident hazards. Certain types of accidents are more likely to occur at one stage of a child's development than at another. Infants under one year need protection against small objects that can be ingested, causing suffocation. They also need to be protected from plastic material that can cause suffocation. Death by falls, fires, and burns also occur in this age group.

Children from one to four years of age are more susceptible to poisoning, drowning, and toy and play equipment accidents.

Accidents happen to children for various reasons -- often a specific chain of events will lead to an accident or injury. Frequently, the hazard is too accessible or too attractive for a child to resist, such as a bottle of aspirin or colored pills, a sharp knife, an unguarded window, or a loaded gun.

Toy Selection

RISK FACTORS
- It is estimated that over 100,000 children under 15 years of age are treated annually in emergency hospital rooms for toy-related injuries.

CONTRIBUTING FACTORS
- choking
- electrocution
- strangulation
- suffocation

COMMENT

Choose toys with care. Keep in mind the child's age, interests, and skill level.

Look for quality design and construction in all toys.

Make sure that all directions or instructions are clear to you and to the child. Discard the plastic wrappings on toys immediately.

Read all labels on toys. Look for age recommendations, such as "not recommended for children under three." Look for other safety labels including: "non-toxic" on painted toys, "flame retardant/flame resistant" on fabric products, and "washable/hygienic materials" on stuffed toys and dolls.

Check all toys periodically for breakage and other hazards. Toys of brittle plastic or glass can easily be broken, exposing dangerous sharp edges. Wooden, metal, and plastic toys that are poorly constructed sometimes have sharp edges as well. A dangerous toy should be thrown away or repaired immediately.

SAFETY SENSE

- Be wary of tiny toys and toys with small removable parts -- they can be swallowed or become lodged in a child's windpipe, ears, or nose. Some squeeze toys have squeakers that can be removed and possibly swallowed. Watch for seams on poorly-constructed stuffed dolls or animals -- they can break open and release small pellets that can be swallowed or inhaled.
- Be aware that toy caps and some noise-making guns can damage hearing. In some jurisdictions, the law requires the following label on boxes of caps producing noise above

a certain level: "WARNING -- Do not fire closer than 30 cm (12 in.) to the ear. Do not use indoors."

- Be wary of electric toys that are improperly constructed, wired, or misused -- they can cause shocks or burns. Electric toys must meet mandatory requirements for maximum surface temperatures and electrical construction. They must also have prominent warning labels. Electric toys with heating elements are recommended only for children over eight years old. Teach your children to use electric toys cautiously and under adult supervision.

- Watch for pins and staples on dolls' clothes, hair, and accessories, as they can puncture an unsuspecting child. Teddy bears and other stuffed toys may have barbed eyes or wired limbs which can cut a child.

- Beware of allowing a child to play with projectiles and other flying toys -- they can be used as weapons and can injure eyes in particular. Don't allow children to play with adult hobby or sporting equipment that has sharp points. Arrows or darts used by children should have soft cork tips, rubber suction cups, or other protective tips.

- Toys that may be safe for older children can be extremely dangerous in the hands of young ones.

Childproofing

RISK FACTORS

• Three percent of all poisoning deaths by solids, liquids, gases, and vapors occur to youngsters aged zero to 15. Death by mechanical suffocation caused by lack of air and plastic bag accounts for six percent.

CONTRIBUTING FACTORS

• ingestion of objects
• lack of air
• poisoning
• electrocution
• strangulation

COMMENT

Childproofing your home is easy and inexpensive, especially when compared with the value of your most prized possessions -- your children. Using the following check list, search your home, room by room and get rid of all potential hazards.

SAFETY SENSE

BASEMENT	✓	KITCHEN CONT'D	✓	BATHROOM CONT'D	✓
Laundry products		Spray cans, deodorizers		Toiletries	
Workbench		Vitamins and other drugs		Medicines	
Ironing board		Appliances, stove knobs		Rubber mats	
Refrigerator, freezer		**DINING ROOM**		Hot water	
KITCHEN		Tablecloth, candles		First-aid supplies	
Knives and other utensils		Heavy objects		**MASTER BEDROOM**	
Cleaning supplies		**BATHROOM**		Beauty products	
Boxes, bottles		Appliances		Handbags, sewing kits	

MASTER BEDROOM CONT'D	✔	HOUSE AREA CONT'D	✔	HOUSE AREA CONT'D	✔
Jewelry, scarves, belts		Small or overhead objects		Porch, balcony railings	
Drugs, contraceptives		Weapons		Window screens	
Matches, lighters		Floors, stairs, Staircases		Drape or blind cords	
BABY'S ROOM		Safety gates		Fire hazards	
Small ojbects		Carpets, throw rugs		Smoke detectors	
Plastic sheets and bags		Lighting		Fire extinguishers	
Crib pillows		Attic access		Rope ladder	
HOUSE AREA		Outside door		Toys	
Electric outlets, cords		Basement door		Flammables, potentials suffocators	

Baby Walkers

RISK FACTORS
- It is estimated that over 22,000 children receive emergency hospital treatment for injuries received as a result of using baby walkers in North America.
- Falls down stairs account for approximately 80 percent of all walker-related hospital cases.

CONTRIBUTING FACTORS
- tipping over
- trapping fingers
- falling down stairs

COMMENT

Walkers provide exercise for a baby, and may help protect the child who is learning to walk. They must be selected carefully and used safely, however, because accidents can happen. In Canada, all walkers must meet a voluntary safety standard that was implemented in 1989. In fact, you probably will not be able to find a walker in the stores because no manufacturer has designed a walker that meets the standard, and stores have removed those that do not meet the voluntary standard.

SAFETY SENSE

- Be wary of small, flimsy wheels or a narrow base -- they can contribute to tipping.
- Be sure the seat is made of sturdy material -- unbreakable plastic or tough fabric with heavy duty stitching or large snaps.
- Look for protective covers for coiled springs and hinges. Locking devices and screws should have no sharp edges or points.
- Assist the child using the walker to maneuvre on and off carpeting, across thresholds, and around furniture.
- Remove throw rugs -- loose rug fibres can get tangled in the wheels.
- Place gates at the top of all stairwells, or keep stairway doors closed to prevent falls.
- Don't leave a child in a walker unattended.
- Make sure the wheel base is stable. It should be both wider and longer than the frame of the walker.

High Chairs

RISK FACTORS
• Approximately 9,000 North American children each year are treated for injuries resulting from accidents involving high chairs.

CONTRIBUTING FACTORS
• child stands in chair and falls out
• chair collapses
• chair tips over when the child tries to climb up on it
• fingers and hands get pinched in chair components
• cuts and punctures from protruding objects, such as loose bolts and screws

COMMENT

Thousands of injuries associated with high chairs are treated in hospital emergency rooms each year. The majority of these injuries result from falls that occur for the following reasons: the tray disengages when the child is leaning or pushing against it, the child topples from the high chair when standing on it, climbing on it, or reaching for something when in it.

SAFETY SENSE

• Choose a high chair with a wide base for stability. It should have safety straps that are not attached to the tray. Avoid hardware with rough edges or sharp points.
• Always use seat belts.
• Use the high chair in an area free of traffic -- away from doorways, refrigerators, ranges, and other kitchen equipment.
• Check the tray each time it is used to make sure it is properly latched to both sides.

• Supervise the child closely, and instruct other children not to pull on the high chair or climb up on it.
• Be sure that the locking device on a folding chair is secure each time you set the chair up. Check the locking device periodically when the child is in the chair, especially if she/he is very active.
• Make sure the child's hands and fingers are out of the way when attaching and detaching the tray.

Strollers and Carriages

RISK FACTORS
• Approximately 14,000 children a year in North America are treated for injuries resulting from an accident involving a stroller or carriage.

CONTRIBUTING FACTORS
• falls
• pinched fingers, toes, hands, and feet
• equipment that tips over

COMMENT

Take your child with you when shopping for a stroller or carriage. Take him/her for a ride in each of the products you are considering -- your baby can help you decide which stroller is the safest and best to buy.

Your child will enjoy the ride if the backrest is firm and nearly vertical, and if the seat is firm and flat. There should be enough headroom for growth when the canopy is attached.

SAFETY SENSE

• Test strollers and carriages for stability.
• Ensure that the base is wide enough to prevent tipping, even when the baby leans over the side. If it can be adjusted to a reclining position, be sure it does not tip backward when the baby lies down.
• Check to make sure the wheels are large enough in diameter to provide stability.
• Do not overlook canopies and shopping baskets attached to strollers -- they can also affect stability.
• Ensure that the canopy locks in a forward horizontal position. When it is unlocked, it should rotate to a downward position at the rear of the stroller.
• The shopping basket for carrying packages should be low on the back of the stroller, and located so that its center is in front of, or directly over, the axle of the rear wheels.
• Check the latching devices to make sure they are securely fastened when using the stroller.
• Make sure the brake operates properly.
• Always use seat belts.
• Do not allow a child to stand in the shopping basket.
• Supervise children when they are in and around strollers.

Playpens

RISK FACTORS
• It is estimated that over 2,500 children receive medical attention each year in North America for injuries received in playpen accidents.

CONTRIBUTING FACTORS
• falls
• cuts and punctures from protruding objects
• strangulation

COMMENT

When the toddler can climb over the side of the playpen, it is time to stop using it. Accidents can happen, however, well before the child reaches this point. Some of the potential mishaps are: the child may fall when trying to climb out of the playpen, especially if it has sides made of large open-weave netting; buttons and snaps on the child's clothing may catch on this netting, causing strangulation; fingers can be pinched in hinges if the playpen does not lock properly; protruding bolts and rough edges can cause cuts, scratches, and bruises.

SAFETY SENSE

• If your playpen has wooden slats, check to make sure the slats are no more than 5.5 cm (2 3/8 in.) apart.
• If the slats are spaced more than 5.5 cm (2 3/8 in.) apart, interweave sheeting between them and fasten securely.
• Make sure that hinges and latches on folding models lock tightly to prevent them from collapsing when the playpen is in use.
• If your playpen has legs, ensure that it has a firm floor support to prevent collapse.
• Use a foam pad in your playpen -- it will last a long time and won't mildew.
• If your playpen has mesh netting, make sure it has a small weave -- smaller than the tiny buttons on a baby's clothing.
• Always take the playpen inside after using it outdoors, to avoid rust, water, and sun damage.
• Remove large toys, bumper pads, or boxes from inside the playpen if you think your child may use them for climbing.
• Avoid tying decorative items across the top of the playpen since they can also be used for climbing.
• If you hang toys from the side of the playpen, ensure that the cord is no longer than 30 cm (12 in.). It should be too short to wrap around the child's neck.

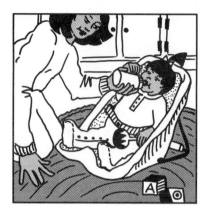

Baby Carriers
(Feeding Seats)

RISK FACTORS

• An estimated 3,000 injuries in North America are treated in hospital emergency rooms each year can be attributed to baby carriers.

CONTRIBUTING FACTORS

• the child is left unattended
• the chair tips over

COMMENT

Baby carriers are convenient for feeding a baby, and for carrying her/him comfortably from place to place. Carriers allow infants to feel that they are part of the activity going on around them.

They can be dangerous, however. Falls are common. To avoid them, follow these safety sense tips.

SAFETY SENSE

• Stay within an arm's reach of the baby when the carrier is on tables, counters, couches, and chairs. Never turn your back. Slippery surfaces, such as glass table tops, can be especially hazardous.
• Attach rough-surfaced adhesive strips to provide a non-skid bottom for the baby carrier.
• Make sure that the baby carrier has a wide, sturdy base that won't tip over easily.
• Always use seat belts.
• Check supporting devices which snap on the back of the baby carrier. They can pop out, causing the carrier to collapse.
• Never use a baby carrier as a substitute for a car seat.

Baby Back Carriers

RISK FACTORS
• No North American data available.

CONTRIBUTING FACTORS
• falls
• reduced blood circulation
• poor quality equipment

COMMENT

Hiking, walking, and shopping are all much easier when you carry your child in an infant back carrier. Framed back carriers should not, however, be used before a baby is four or five months old. Before that age, the baby's neck is not usually strong enough to withstand jolts that could injure it.

SAFETY SENSE

• Make sure your baby fits properly in the carrier. Try it on with the baby in it and check for enough depth in the back so the baby won't slip out. Leg openings should be small enough to prevent the baby from slipping out, but large enough to avoid chafing the baby's legs.
• Ensure that your carrier has restraining straps to prevent your child from climbing out.
• Look for a carrier made of sturdy materials. It should have reinforced stitching and large, heavy-duty snaps.
• Avoid joints that may accidentally

close and pinch or cut the baby.
• Avoid sharp points, edges, or rough surfaces.
• Look for a carrier with soft, padded covering over the metal frame near the baby's face.
• Check the carrier periodically for ripped seams, missing or loose snaps, frayed seats or straps, and repair immediately.
• Be careful that the baby does not fall out when you lean over or stoop. Bend from the knees rather than the waist.
• Use the seat belt on the carrier at all times.

Toy Boxes (Chests)

RISK FACTORS
• It is estimated that over 5,000 persons in North America are injured each year as a result of using a toy box or chest. Seventy percent of those injured are under the age of five.

CONTRIBUTING FACTORS
• falls against the box
• hands and arms cut by a falling lid
• entrapment of the head by a falling lid

COMMENT

Most toy box injuries are lacerations and occur when a child falls against the corner or edge of the box. Hinged lids on toy boxes pose another serious hazard -- a heavy lid can fall with great force on a child. The child could receive a serious neck injury from the blow, and could also be trapped inside the box without proper ventilation.

If you plan to purchase a toy box or if you already own one, consider the following advice.

SAFETY SENSE

• If you are buying a box with a hinged lid, be sure that the lid is lightweight, has a flat inner surface, and that it has a device to hold it open safely in a raised position. Lids with protrusions or recessed areas on the inside may make it more difficult for a child to get free if the lid closes on her/his head. Make sure that the device holding the lid will not pinch.
• Check regularly for rough or sharp edges on all metal components and for splinters and other rough areas on wooden boxes.
• Rounded, padded edges and corners may prevent some injuries. Check padding occasionally and repair if necessary.
• Make sure that the toy box is well-ventilated. There should be ample ventilation holes in the lid and sides. You may prefer to buy a box with a lid that cannot close completely.
• Do not use a toy box with a lid that locks.
• Reduce the chance of a serious injury being caused by a fall against the box. Don't put the box in a heavily travelled area; caution your children against running or roughhousing near it. As much as possible, keep the area around the toy box free of clutter. The toy box should be firmly placed on a non-slippery surface.
• Remove the lid of the box if you feel it may be hazardous in any way.
• Check periodically to make sure that the device holding the lid open is in good working order.
• If your toy box is homemade, check it carefully for the hazards discussed above. If you are planning to build one, keep them in mind.

Electrically-operated Toys

RISK FACTORS
• No North American data available. However, toy-related accidents account for an estimated 125,000 emergency room visits each year.

CONTRIBUTING FACTORS
• electric shock
• burns
• cuts
• punctures
• pinching

COMMENT

Electrically-operated toys intended for children can be extremely hazardous. The dangers are burns, especially if the product has a heating element, and a wide variety of mechanical hazards common to toys in general, such as sharp edges, points, and moving parts. Although there are product regulations governing the manufacturing of electrical toys, adults should buy these products selectively. It is essential to supervise their use in the home, and repair or discard them at the first sign of serious deterioration.

SAFETY SENSE

• Do not buy an electrical toy for a child who is too young to use it safely. Always check the minimum age recommendation on the package. If a toy is labelled "not recommended for children under eight years of age," this does not necessarily mean that every child who is eight years old is mature enough to operate it.

• Read the accompanying instructions carefully with any child who will be using the product. Be sure that the child knows how to use the item safely, understands all the instructions and warning labels, and is aware of the hazards of misusing the

toy. Keep the instructions in a safe place where they can be easily found.

• Supervise the use of any electrical product. Consider both the maturity of the child and the nature of the toy when deciding just how much supervision is necessary.

• Be sure that the plug of an electrical product fits snugly into wall outlets or (if they must be used) extension cord receptacles. No prongs should be exposed. Teach children to disconnect an electrical appliance by grasping the plug, not by pulling on the cord.

• Keep infants and toddlers out of the area in which an electrical toy is being

used.
- Put electrical toys away immediately after use in a dry storage area, out of the reach of younger children.
- Check on the condition of these toys periodically. Be alert for broken parts, frayed cords, and damage to wiring and other protected components.

- Adults should replace light bulbs on electrical toys to ensure that the replacement bulb is the proper wattage. Disconnect the plug before changing the bulb.
- Discard immediately any product that has been so severely damaged that it cannot be repaired.

SENIOR SAFETY

Any house or apartment should provide for the comfort, safety, and protection of the occupants and should take into account the need for privacy, independence, and freedom of movement. People of all ages have more or less the same needs, but good housing is especially important for older people who wish to live independently.

Builders today are designing homes for the senior market. These homes incorporate all the frills into a small space. An important consideration is to make the space and everything in it accessible. Many of the safety sense ideas that are presented in this unit can be adapted to an existing home or incorporated into a new home where seniors will live.

Lighting and Heating Systems

RISK FACTORS
- Falls are the greatest cause of death in the over 55 age bracket, accounting for over 55 percent of all fatalities in North America. Death by fire accounts for four percent of the deaths in this age bracket.

CONTRIBUTING FACTORS
- poor lighting
- improperly shielded heating appliances
- fire

COMMENT

Good lighting is important in any home, but especially so in homes of the elderly because of their failing eyesight. A study done in California on housing for the retired and aged showed that the most flagrant and consistent violations of good house design were in the area of lighting. There were problems with the intensity, amount, and kind of light being installed.

To have good lighting, you don't need to buy expensive lamps or fixtures. What you need is the right kind of light in the right place. Proper lighting can cheer up and brighten a room, which in turn makes people feel better.

The need for bodily warmth becomes more acute as we age, so heating systems in the home are an important consideration for the elderly. Check the following safety sense lighting and heating tips for a safe home.

SAFETY SENSE

- Provide ample lighting for outside steps, walks, driveways, interior stairways, hallways, and all rooms.
- Ensure that three-way switches are located at the entrances to a room, just inside the door.
- Install night lights in the bedroom and bathroom. A switch or lamp should be located within reach of the bed. Luminous cover plates for switches make them easy to locate.

- Make sure that all light is distributed evenly, without glare.
- Have local light available for specific tasks such as reading, sewing, hobbies, food preparation, and taking medicine. Lights inside closets and storage areas assist visibility.
- Use fixtures that are easy to clean and bulbs that are easy to change. Portable lamps and pull-down ceiling or wall lamps can be changed without

a step ladder.
- Ensure that electric outlets are placed where they don't interfere with furniture. They should be 71 to 76 cm (28 to 30 in.) off the floor if possible.
- Ensure that fixtures and wiring are well constructed.
- Install lights at the top and bottom of stairs, with switches at both places. If this is not possible, place lights so that all steps are visible.
- Ensure that the heating system distributes heat evenly between 24 to 26° C (75 to 80° F) in every room.
- Shield radiators to prevent burns.
- Avoid using portable room heaters if possible -- they can be hazardous. Heating systems and room heaters should be serviced once a year.
- Install a ceiling heat lamp in the bath for increased comfort.
- Paint walls light colors -- they require less artificial or supplemental light than do darker walls.

Furniture

RISK FACTORS
• Over 1.5 million people a year, many of them elderly, receive medical attention for injuries received from home furnishings, fixtures, and accessories in North America. Millions of other injuries go unreported.

CONTRIBUTING FACTORS
• bumping into furniture
• tripping over furniture
• pinching fingers and hands

COMMENT

With the exception of furniture for hospitals or institutions, no special attention has been given to the design of furniture for the elderly. This is unfortunate, since elderly people spend so much time sitting. You can make an elderly person more comfortable by considering the following points.

SAFETY SENSE

• Avoid bruises by using furniture with rounded edges and corners.
• Be aware that small pieces of furniture may be used as an occasional support. They should be stable enough to bear the weight of an adult.
• Ensure that furniture is light enough to move easily for cleaning. Glider tips or casters that do not slide too freely can be placed on all heavy pieces, including the bed.
• Use chairs that give good body support for the lower back and neck.
• Ensure that chairs fit the persons using them, and that they do not cut off circulation when both feet are flat on the floor.
• Ensure that chair arms extend far enough forward to allow leverage when a person is sitting down or

getting up. Cut the legs down if necessary.
• Keep high-traffic areas clear of furniture to prevent falls.
• Use furniture that does not clutter up the room. There should be enough space around the bed so it can be made easily.
• Use fabrics in home furnishings that are easily cleaned, stain resistant, flame-resistant, non-allergenic, and that allow for ventilation.
• Build a stop into drawers so they cannot be accidentally pulled all the way out.
• Ensure that doors and drawers operate smoothly.
• Provide storage areas that are between hip and eye level, to ensure accessibility without stooping, reaching, or climbing.

Bathroom and Bedroom

RISK FACTORS

• In North America, it is estimated that two percent of all accidental falls in the senior age group happen in the bathroom. An estimated six percent of all falls occur in the bedroom.

CONTRIBUTING FACTORS

• slipping on tub surface or wet floor
• losing balance when climbing into tub
• tripping over furniture and clothing

COMMENT

It is important to have bathroom furnishings in the proper location in order to prevent the elderly from experiencing falls, burns, scalds, and poisonings.

SAFETY SENSE

• Ensure that the bathtub is located away from the window and drafts.
• Provide a low bathtub with a flat, skid-resistant bottom, rubber mat, or abrasive strips.
• Install well-anchored grab bars, 100 cm (40 in.) above the floor, over the tub or in the shower. A portable grab bar can also be put on the edge of tub.
• Use towel racks of metal or wood, securely attached to wall studs.
• Have a stool, bench, or seat for use in the tub or shower.
• Install a shower with mixing controls, preferably thermostatic mixing valves, to prevent scalds.
• Ensure that you can open the bathroom door from the outside. The light switch should be located outside the door.
• If possible, locate the bathroom next

to the bedroom and away from steps or stairways.
• Mark medicines for internal use with a red cross, and medicines for external use with another color. Store them separately to avoid confusion.
• Provide a large bedside table for medicines, water, light, and other items.
• Ensure that access to the bathroom is direct and clear of furniture.
• Ensure that there is one door or window at least 60 cm (24 in.) wide and no more than 90 cm (36 in.) above the floor in the sleeping area in case of fire. You should be able to open screens and storms from the outside.
• Make sure you have a smoke detector in the hallway, close to bedroom entrances.

Kitchen

RISK FACTORS

• The kitchen is the location for approximately 23 percent of all home accidents in North America.

CONTRIBUTING FACTORS

• burns and scalds
• falls
• cuts
• fire

COMMENT

The kitchen is the scene of many injuries and should always be designed with safety and convenience in mind. Burns, scalds, and cuts are common types of accidents in the kitchen. Consider these factors when planning a kitchen for an elderly person.

SAFETY SENSE

• Ensure that at least one counter is built low enough to accommodate a person working in a sitting position.
• If possible, place the oven at waist level so that stooping or excessive reaching is not necessary.
• Ensure that overhead cabinet shelves are not more than 30 cm (12 in.) deep or higher than 180 cm (72 in.) above the floor. Don't use cabinets that are located over the refrigerator or stove.
• Have adequate ventilation to eliminate hot air and cooking odors.
• Install lights over the sink, counters, and range.
• If possible, make sure the edges and corners of counters, tables, and other equipment are rounded.
• Use cabinets with sliding doors on upper cupboards if possible, and vertical pull-out racks or drawers in lower cabinets.

• If you have an electric stove, the controls should be located so you don't have to reach across hot elements to use them.
• Vent gas heating appliances to the outside, and inspect them periodically. People with a diminished sense of smell are sometimes unable to detect escaping gas.
• Mark burner controls and other knob dials on appliances with bright colors to indicate on/off and different speeds.
• Store household cleaners and insecticides away from food items.
• Get rid of all kitchen utensils and equipment that is not safe to use.
• Use non-skid floor wax, and wipe up spilled liquids or grease right away.
• Refer to pages 1 to 14 in the Kitchen Section for additional safety sense ideas in the kitchen.

Steps, Stairways, and Floors

RISK FACTORS
• Stairs, landings, floors, and ramps are the most common locations of falls. They are involved in about 50 percent of all injuries related to home structures.

CONTRIBUTING FACTORS
• tripping
• falling down stairs
• climbing to reach some article
• falling off chairs
• slipping on surfaces

COMMENT

A stairway in the home can be a booby trap for a person of any age, but mishaps on the stairs are more likely to result in serious injury or death to the elderly. Make stairways less hazardous by building them safely, keeping them in good condition, and using them safely.

Elderly people often trip and fall on flat floors as well, so make sure floors are as safe as possible.

SAFETY SENSE

• Ensure that stairways are not too steep. Risers should be uniform in height and treads should be uniform in width. The optimum height for risers for elderly people is 15 cm (6 in.).
• Attach handrails on both sides of stairways. They should extend from top to bottom with finished ends that won't catch on clothing.
• Build short flights of stairs with landings rather than a single straight flight.
• Prevent falls by using non-slip treads or carpeting on stairs. Outside walks and steps should have a surface that is not slippery when wet.
• Avoid using one-step elevation changes. If you have floors at different heights, use a ramp. The rise should not exceed 5 cm (2 in.) in 30 cm (12 in.).

• Use non-skid backs or non-skid pads with scatter rugs.
• Ensure that traffic areas have a smooth, even floor. Suitable flooring materials include unglazed tile, cork, unwaxed vinyl, asbestos tile, unwaxed wood, or wall-to-wall carpeting. If floors are waxed, a special slip-resistant wax should be used.
• Ensure that all carpets, rugs, or linoleum lie smoothly. If necessary, tack them down at the edges.
• Paint the top and bottom step of a stairway white or another light color to indicate the start and finish of the stairs.
• Consider marking the edge of the step with fluorescent tape or painting the riser a contrasting color.
• Wear footwear that fits properly. Avoid sticky crepe or rubber soled shoes.

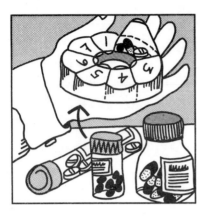

Medications

RISK FACTORS
- An estimated 50,000 North Americans die each year as a result of the side effects of drugs.
- Approximately two million seniors are treated each year for reactions to drugs.
- Seniors take an average of six prescription drugs and three over-the-counter drugs at any one time.

CONTRIBUTING FACTORS
- overdosing
- mixing different medications
- taking medications that have expired
- borrowing medications from friends
- sampling different medications not prescribed
- taking medication that was wrongly prescribed

COMMENT

People over 65 years of age represent about ten percent of the population and use approximately 40 percent of the prescription medications dispensed annually. This is because seniors as a group have more long-term illnesses than younger North Americans. Because seniors can have several medical problems at a time, they often take more than one type of drug per day. When taking more than one drug at a time, the combined effect of all the drugs can produce different physical and mental reactions, such as disorientation, dizziness, and even heart, liver, and kidney failure.

SAFETY SENSE

- Return all unused medication to your doctor or pharmacist.
- Follow the prescribed dosage listed on the container.
- If you cannot read the directions on the container, ask the pharmacist to use larger type or have someone administer the dosage for you.
- Never take a friend's medication, even if it is for a similar ailment.
- Always inform your doctor or pharmacist about past problems with any drugs. Keep a personal record of drugs that affect you in a bad way.
- Keep a daily record of all the drugs you are taking -- even over-the-counter ones like allergy pills, cough syrups, etc.

- Ask your doctor or pharmacist about the side effects of the medication. Some medications will effect your walking and driving ability.
- Store all your medications in a safe place, away from children.
- Use dosage containers available at drug stores. These containers help you to remember when to take a specific drug. These containers are particularly useful if you take more than one drug each day.
- Finish taking the recommended amount of tablets as prescribed by your doctor or pharmacist. Failure to complete the prescription can result in further complications.

Violent Crimes

RISK FACTORS

* Fewer than two percent of all personal attacks are against seniors.

CONTRIBUTING FACTORS

* robbery
* assault

COMMENT

Although violent crimes against seniors are relatively infrequent, older people generally feel particularly vulnerable to physical attack. This fear rises out of the fact that they may not be as strong or agile as when they were young, nor do they have the power to defend themselves or to run away. To increase their feeling of safety and security, seniors should do the following.

SAFETY SENSE

* Trim trees and bushes that may block the view from doors and windows.
* Turn on exterior lights at night.
* If you have a garage, keep the garage door closed and locked.
* Arrange for a friend to call you once a day.
* Buy dead bolts or heavy duty locks for your doors.
* Make sure windows and patio doors are secured, but ensure that you can still escape in the event of a fire.
* Consider installing a burglar alarm in your home. Have an emergency button installed with it.
* Be assertive when walking on the street.
* Walk in well-lit and well-travelled areas.
* Avoid walking alone and plan shopping trips with a friend.
* Avoid walking at night.
* Avoid walking in laneways and try to stay close to the street where it is busy.
* Exercise a healthy caution of strangers.

SPECIALTY TOPICS

APARTMENTS

Often we think that an apartment dwelling is safer than a single-family home because there are usually plenty of people close by. This is not, in fact, so. Apartments are just as susceptible to criminal activity, such as robbery, rape, and murder, as are other dwellings. If you now live in an apartment, or will be thinking about moving into one someday, consider the following safety sense items.

SAFETY SENSE

- Do not move into an apartment that does not have security locks on all outside doors. If the apartment you now live in does not have security doors, pressure the management to install them.
- If lights are dimmed or bulbs are burned out, notify management and insist they be replaced. Lighting is important as a deterrent to crime.
- If possible, choose an apartment with an in-house superintendent who can be reached in case of an emergency.
- Be aware that underground parking areas can be dangerous. Apartment complexes should have security ga-

rage doors and they should be well lit.
- Install a peephole in your door for screening visitors. Do not open your door to people you do not know.
- Never open the security doors, either from your apartment or at the door, to anyone you do not know by voice. Criminals may pose as salespeople, maintenance workers, etc., to get into a building.
- Form an apartment "Crime Watch" group. Consult your local police force for more information on how to establish one.

185

BABY'S BUMPS AND FALLS

The first year of baby's life is one of amazing growth and development. Turn your back for a moment, and the infant who was squirming helplessly on a blanket is suddenly crawling across the room at high speed. Even as you delight in your child's new skills and independence, remember that these changes increase the risk of injury from accidental falls.

In the infant age group, falls are among the most common, and the most serious, kind of accident. Skull fractures and facial scrapes and bruises top the list of injuries.

Most infant falls occur when babies are between five and 11 months old. Children learn to roll from the abdomen to the back at three and five months of age, and from the back to the tummy at six months to a year. It's this developmental step that increases their risk.

SAFETY SENSE

- Put away for a while any table that isn't sturdy. A strong baby may be able to pull him- or herself up to a table and edge around it, but can't tell the difference between a sturdy table and a wobbly one.
- Keep baby out of the bathroom when you aren't around. The tile floors and ceramic tub are particularly dangerous surfaces because they are both slippery and hard.
- Don't just close doors; lock them. Just because the baby doesn't have the wrist strength to open the basement door today doesn't mean she/he won't tomorrow.
- Remember that electrical cords, corners of rugs, or uneven boards in a wooden floor can upset a baby's delicate balance.
- Don't bother with shoes for little babies except in the coldest weather; hard, slippery soles and heavy shoes and socks only increase the chances of slipping. Rubber soles can catch,

especially on a rug.
- Be sure that overall cuffs and pajama feet aren't interfering with your baby's ability to get around.
- Never leave a baby alone on a diapering table, even with safety straps. Straps do break occasionally. Have a fresh diaper ready before beginning to change the baby.
- Buy a good playpen and don't hesitate to put the infant in it. Playpens with mesh sides are safe and allow the baby to look out without being able to climb out.
- Close off stairs with an infant gate mounted on one wall that can be stretched across the landing when the baby is awake. Be sure to install the gate correctly; children have been known to slip under them.
- Pad the ends and sharp corners of end and coffee tables. Better yet, remove them from the living area until the youngster is skilled at walking.

BARBECUES

Backyard or balcony barbecuing is as much a rite of summer as baseball, mosquitoes, and sunburn.

In the past few years, more and more people have been sizzling their steaks and broiling their burgers over a gas flame rather than charcoal. While gas barbecues are cleaner and faster than charcoal, both kinds present a potential hazard to the careless user.

SAFETY SENSE

- When you purchase a propane barbecue, be sure it carries the label of a recognized testing organization to ensure it has been tested and found acceptable.
- A gas barbecue is meant to be used outdoors. Do not take it indoors except for temporary storage.
- Never use charcoal or similar barbecue fuel inside any building, boat, recreational vehicle or other enclosed area. It produces carbon monoxide.
- Lift the lid of the barbecue before you light it to prevent excess gas from exploding.
- Light the barbecue the moment the gas flow is turned on.
- Once a month, and each time the gas line has been reconnected, check for leaks at the valve assembly joint with the "soapy water test."
- Never refill a tank that is corroded, leaking or showing signs of obvious physical damage.

- When you're through cooking with a propane barbecue, turn off the main valve on the propane cylinder as well as the heat control valves.
- Install a propane safety valve which monitors the amount of gas flowing through your system. If the flow of gas increases beyond safe conditions, the valve will sense the problem and shut off the flow of propane at the tank.
- Never substitute gasoline, kerosene or naphtha for lighting fluid on a charcoal barbecue. These highly flammable fuels will flare up quickly and may even ignite the fuel can if it isn't removed quickly enough.
- Always read and follow the directions on the barbecue lighter fluid package.
- Leave coals for approximately five minutes to soak up the fluid before trying to light the barbecue. If you squirt fluid on the coals and light them immediately, the fuel will flare up but

then die out just as quickly. If this happens, never add more fire starter before the coals have died out completely; the burst of flames may travel up the stream of volatile fluid, causing the can to explode.

- The safest starters are chemicals in cake form, or an electric charcoal starter.
- Keep small children away from the barbecue at all times.
- After you've finished cooking, soak the coals in water. Coals that seem dead can reignite a day later.
- Never keep damp or wet charcoal in a poorly ventilated area. As they dry, it is possible for coals to burst spontaneously into flame.
- Be aware that, in most jurisdictions, barbecues are not allowed on apartment balconies as the confined space can cause a build-up of carbon monoxide gas.

- Do not place any kind of barbecue within 3 m (10 ft.) of a combustible wall or window of a building, such as a wooden cottage.
- Store electrical barbecues in a protected location or cover them completely when they are not in use. Also make sure they are unplugged.
- Examine the electric heater element regularly; if it shows signs of wear and corrosion, have it replaced immediately.
- To prevent damage to the barbecue's cord, ensure it is routed away from the hot surfaces. Use the proper size and type of extension cord to reach the outlet, and check both the barbecue's cord and the extension cord periodically for damage.
- Never place an electric barbecue near a swimming pool. It could topple over into the water and electrocute anyone in the pool.

CARBON MONOXIDE

Because you can't see it, taste it, or smell it, carbon monoxide (CO) has earned the name, "the silent killer." You may think you can smell it when you're actually smelling the smoke and other fire-produced gases associated with it. Carbon monoxide is not a product of the automobile alone. Whenever any fuel is burned, CO is usually one of the products. If it escapes into the rooms of your home, the air you breathe can kill you.

As you breathe, the oxygen in the air combines with your blood and is carried to all parts of your body. If your supply of oxygen is reduced, your brain cells will be the first to be affected; weakness, dizziness, and confusion will result. Further oxygen starvation will ultimately result in death.

As you breathe air containing CO, the gas crowds out the oxygen and produces the results described above. Because carbon monoxide combines with your blood 200 times more readily than oxygen, a relatively small amount can displace the life-giving oxygen you need. Even if CO doesn't kill you, it can lead to permanent brain damage.

SAFETY SENSE

- Don't close your fireplace damper until you are certain the fire is out. If smoke enters the room, it may mean that your furnace is causing a reverse flow. Opening a window will help to prevent this from happening.
- Have your heating systems -- furnace, space heater, fireplace and incinerator -- checked annually to make sure they are operating efficiently and that vents, pipes, flues and chimneys are tight. These represent common-sense precautions against fire, too.
- Make certain that your heating plant is not starved for air; heating devices, especially central furnaces, require a lot of air for proper operation. Check with your heating or fuel supplier to be sure.
- Never use charcoal grills indoors. Any time a fuel-consuming device is used in an enclosed area, it is using up oxygen and may be producing CO.
- Never alter a heating device by changing its ducts or vent pipes in order to get more heat out of it.
- When changing from one type of fuel to another, have all appliances involved adjusted by a qualified service person.

189

- If you have an attached garage, make certain that it is well sealed off from the rest of the house.
- Never run your car engine in a closed garage.
- Never use a heating device designed for venting until it has been properly vented to the outside.
- Use only heating devices that bear the label of a nationally-recognized testing laboratory. Follow the manufacturers' recommendations concerning their installation and use.
- Although it's not 100% reliable, use your nose as a detection device. It won't detect the presence of CO, but may smell accompanying smoke. Track down unexplained sources of smoke at once; after you've located them, have the trouble remedied immediately.
- Have all chimneys inspected and cleaned at least once every two years -- more often if you burn wood.
- Have propane refrigerators serviced regularly, including those used at the cottage. If your propane refrigerator is currently vented to the inside, have it vented outside immediately.

CHAIN SAWS

A chain saw is a power tool that can be invaluable for cutting up firewood for those long winter nights. But, as with all power tools, if handled improperly, it can cause serious injury. Fortunately for chain saw users, advances in technology have made them safer. New models are equipped with a combination of features designed to reduce the major cause of severe chainsaw injuries: kickback, an upward or backward jerking motion of the saw. Although kickback is the single biggest cause of chainsaw injuries, three-fourths of the injuries are caused by a variety of other factors -- usually some kind of operator error. If you use a chainsaw, follow these safety sense precautions.

SAFETY SENSE

- Wear protective clothing, including a hard hat, safety goggles, gloves that provide a good grip, hearing protectors, safety shoes, and snug-fitting clothes that won't get caught in the chain.
- Before you begin, make sure your saw is in good repair. Clear your work area of debris so the chain won't touch anything but the wood you want to cut.
- Keep your saw sharp. A sharp blade is more likely to cut through a log and less likely to catch on it.
- Make sure you have the right chainsaw for the job. Your owner's manual should explain your saw's capabilities.
- Do not work alone. An extra pair of hands will make some dangerous situations safe, and if you are injured, the other person can get help.
- Always start the saw according to

your manual's directions. Carry the saw with the blade pointing backwards when not using it, and never carry a saw that is running.
- Stand to the side of the saw so you won't follow through into your leg, and so that if it kicks back, it will fly past you, not into you. Always be aware of what is in the saw's downward path after the cut.
- Stand on the uphill side of a log so it won't roll into you. Watch for branches that may spring back as you cut.
- Let the saw do the work; don't force it through the cut.
- If you must refuel a gasoline-powered saw, let it cool first, and clean up any spills. Avoid the hot muffler as you work. If your saw is electric, make sure you use an extension cord approved for outside use, and don't use the saw in a damp environment.
- If you are a weekend lumberjack,

don't tackle a cutting job that involves climbing trees. Many amateurs have fallen out of trees or had large branches fall on them while using a chainsaw. Save the big jobs for professionals.

- Don't touch the tip of the guide bar to any object. Before you saw through a branch or log, check for nearby branches that could come in contact with the saw.
- Don't bury the tip in a cut, and don't remove the tip guard to make a bigger cut.
- Hold the saw firmly with both hands. Keep your left arm straight so that, in case of kickback, the saw will rise in front of you instead of back into you.

Never hold a running saw with one hand -- a one-hand grip provides the saw with an easy pivot point if it jerks back.

- Avoid cutting tree limbs above mid-chest height.
- Finally, remember that every chain saw is different; you need to know your saw's particular features. The instruction manual that comes with the chainsaw contains good information about safety. Read through the manual before you start. Too many people read it just far enough to find out how to start the saw, and miss information that may be vital to their safety.

CHRISTMAS TREES AND ORNAMENTS

Christmas trees, lights, and other seasonal accessories can create a magical and memorable holiday. These sensible suggestions will help ensure your holiday memories remain magical.

If you purchase a natural tree, pick one that's fresh; a dry tree can be particularly hazardous. Test for freshness by rubbing a hand over the branches or by tapping the base of the tree on the ground. If needles start to fall, do not buy the tree.

SAFETY SENSE

- If cutting your own tree, be extra careful how you wield the axe or use the saw.
- Store the tree outdoors, preferably in the shade, until ready to use it.
- Recut the trunk diagonally and mount the base of the tree securely.
- Keep the base of a natural tree in water. Check the water level daily and add more as required.
- Keep all types of trees away from fireplaces, heaters, and other sources of heat.
- Declare the tree a non-smoking area, and keep matches out of the hands of children.
- Do not put your tree where it blocks an exit.
- Never leave small children alone with a Christmas tree.
- Never use electric light strings on metallic trees. Instead, shine a spot- or floodlight for a colorful effect.
- Don't leave the Christmas tree lights on if no one is in the room.
- If a tree catches fire, do not attempt to move it. Put the fire out with an extinguisher if you can. If not, eva-
cuate the building, and call the fire department.
- Before you replace a bulb, allow it to cool off. Make sure you unplug the light string.
- Be sure to check that bulb reflectors have insulation, consisting of either plastic or another non-metallic material, placed between the lamp and the metal part of the reflector. The reflector is often sold with the Christmas light string.
- Before using any Christmas tree lights or electric decoration, check all wiring, sockets, and plugs for fraying, cracks, or loose connections. If at all in doubt, replace the old sets.
- When buying replacement bulbs, make sure they have the correct wattage and/or voltage.
- If hanging lights outside, be sure to use light strings that are specially designed for outdoor use.
- Do not use metallic fastening devices, such as nails or tacks, to hold strings of outdoor lights in place. Use insulated staples instead, and be careful not to pierce the wire insulation.

DO-IT-YOURSELF INSULATION

It's rare these days to find a home-owner who hasn't heard about the benefits of home insulation. In these energy-conscious times, more and more people are turning down their thermostats and water heaters, wearing extra clothes indoors, and, of course, insulating their homes.

Insulating a house is practical, economical, and important -- it not only saves you money, but conserves the energy resources of the country.

Insulation offers protection against the elements, particularly in extreme temperatures -- either hot or cold. Insulation can reduce heating and electric bills, and, if you install it yourself, can save you even more money. However, do-it-yourselfers should pay close attention to the potential health and safety hazards of insulation.

SAFETY SENSE

- Wear goggles while you work. Irritating fibres can make your eyes itchy and sometimes cause permanent damage.
- Plan your work for cooler days to avoid heat stress. When it's hot outside, it's even hotter in the attic.
- Always wear a dust mask. Fibres will irritate your throat and lungs, especially if you're allergy-prone.
- Protect your skin from irritating fibres with long sleeves and gloves; knee pads are also a good idea.
- Plug extension cords into sockets equipped with ground fault circuit interrupters to prevent shock.
- Wear a hard hat to protect your head from low rafters, protruding nails, and other overhead hazards.
- Be sure you don't create fire hazards by improperly installing the insulation. Experts advise that all electrical wires should be placed above the insulation batts.

- When you are working in the attic, lay down some boards at right angles to the joists so that you can walk and lean on them as you work. They should be at least 1.2 to 1.8 m (4 to 6 ft.) long so that they span more than two joists.
- Use a board and a serrated-edged knife or large shears to cut the batts or blankets. Using a sheet knife that attaches to your belt is also a good idea.
- If you are using a ladder, make sure it's in good condition and placed in a level position on the floor.
- Since climbing can't be avoided on attic projects, remember always to keep one hand free for holding on. It's best to have someone pass the insulation up to you.
- If you use extension lights, ensure that they have guards to minimize the possibility of contact between bulb and paper.

ELEVATORS

Elevators are one of the most effort-saving modern inventions, and perhaps one of the most imperfect. Sooner or later, most elevators are going to get stuck or break down.

Being trapped in an apartment elevator may be inconvenient and uncomfortable, but it is usually safe providing there isn't a fire.

SAFETY SENSE

• Remain calm. Since the majority of elevators are in office buildings or home apartments, help is not far off.
• Do not try to escape through the elevator ceiling. If the elevator does start up again you could be seriously injured.
• If you are trapped between floors, look around for a telephone or alarm bell and use it.
• Do not enter an elevator if you feel uncomfortable about the other passengers who are waiting for it. Some crimes do occur on elevators. It's a good idea for women to stand by the alarm panel in case it is needed.
• Never use elevators when the fire alarm has sounded. If smoke or gases get into the shaft you could

suffer carbon monoxide poisoning.
• If you hear unfamiliar sounds when using an elevator, or if the doors close too rapidly, or the elevator doesn't stop level with the floor exit, report the problem. The elevator may need to be serviced.
• Help prevent youngsters from "joy-riding" in elevators. This often causes damage, and the horseplay may lead to accidents.
• Do not enter an overcrowded elevator. Wait the few minutes needed to take the next one.
• When the doors open, enter the elevator promptly and move to the back. This allows all users to get on the elevator without the doors closing on them. Even a door jammed against an ankle can cause injury.

EMERGENCY ESCAPE ROUTES

"What would I do in an emergency such as a fire?" You should ask yourself this question because, much as you hope it won't, it could happen to you. Thousands of fires strike North American homes every year. By planning ahead, you can eliminate those first few minutes of uncertainty that could cost you more than just a home.

A good fire escape plan must be tailor-made for the house. The model escape plan provided at the left is intended only to assist you in creating your own home plan.

Make special provisions for the elderly and the very young by assigning one person to each family member who might need assistance.

SAFETY SENSE

- Hold a family meeting at least once a year and discuss your fire escape plan. If escape routes are planned, the chance of panic will be lessened.
- You should plan for two escape routes for each room.
- Teach children to go immediately to the primary route; if it is blocked, have them use the second route.
- Children must be instructed not to go looking for their parents. Leave the house as quickly as possible.
- All family members should go to a predesignated meeting spot. This will help to determine who is missing.
- Once everyone is accounted for, do not re-enter the house. Call for help from a neighbor's house.
- Families should practice their escape routes at least twice a year. Children require lots of practice and instruction.

FALLS

Falls are the number one killer in the home today, and, after traffic accidents, they are the largest single cause of accidental death in North America.

Every time we lift a foot to take a step, our center of gravity lurches out ahead of us. As the step is taken, we catch up with our center of gravity and, in a moment, have both feet on the ground and under us again. The process of walking, therefore, is one of constant falling and recovering. Sometimes, however, we don't recover, if the next step is a trip or a slip or a miss. The result is often serious injury and, sometimes, death.

SAFETY SENSE

- Watch out for hoses, cords, and wires if they must temporarily be in the traffic area.
- Install well-anchored grab bars and traction mats or strips in bathtubs and showers.
- When carrying packages, be especially alert for obstacles such as divider bars. Never carry anything that blocks your vision.
- Install night lights for those late night treks to the bathroom.
- Keep all walkways clear; insist that people pick up their belongings.
- Keep steps clear of ice and be extra careful on icy sidewalks. Ice-related accidents account for the most falls around the home.
- In garages, attics, basements, and all storage areas, let there be light -- and no clutter.
- Always use sturdy ladders or platforms to reach heights. Never improvise a foot rest to reach out to the side -- move the ladder instead.
- Check wooden ladders for stability and soundness; check aluminum ones for bent legs.
- Avoid working on roofs unless you have a very good sense of balance.
- Wear shoes or slippers in the house. Stockings on a smooth surface are as slippery as a banana peel.
- Change position -- from lying to sitting and sitting to standing -- in stages; pause after each stage.
- Grip something secure when looking or reaching upwards to a high shelf, or stooping to a lower cupboard.
- Always wipe water or grease off the floor immediately.
- Come down stairs one at a time; count them as you go. If it feels safer, come down backwards.
- Install a hand rail on both sides of the stairs.

- Fix knobs or tape to the stairwell to tell you when you have reached the top and bottom of the stairs.
- Wear well-fitting shoes or slippers, not floppy ones.
- If you wear spectacles fitted with bifocal lenses, take special care on the stairs.
- Provide bright lighting in the kitchen, hall, landing, and passages.
- Keep a flashlight handy by the bed.
- Install two-way light switches between the hall and landing.
- Repair or remove frayed edges of carpets, mats, and linoleum; tack loose edges to the floor.
- Use throw rugs with non-skid backs; be sure they lie flat.
- Use non-slip floor polish.

FIREARMS

Each year, millions of North Americans take to the bush, field, and marshes in search of game animals. Millions of others participate in organized target shooting with pistols, rifles, and shotguns, a year-round sport with few restrictions as to weather, time, or place.

Gun clubs throughout the country instruct beginning shooters in safe gun handling. If the rules of safety are practiced constantly under supervision, they become habit with the club shooter.

Home ranges that are properly safeguarded and used with common sense rules of care and caution can provide intriguing family sport. At the same time, they provide the opportunity for parents to instruct their children in safe gun handling.

SAFETY SENSE

- Keep guns in a locked case or rack.
- Store ammunition separately in locked containers in a cool, dry place.
- Have any heirloom or souvenir pistol, shotgun, rifle, cartridge, grenade, or similar item checked by a competent gunsmith to be certain it is safe. Your police department can advise on disposal of explosives or unwanted items.
- Permit only unloaded, open guns to be taken into the home.
- Before a gun is handled for any reason, open the action and check the chamber and magazine to be sure it is unloaded. If a cartridge is present, and you are uncertain how to remove it, store the gun in the open position (it can't fire when open) and keep it far away from children until someone who is familiar with guns can remove the cartridge.
- Do not try to operate a gun's mechanism (action) unless you know how it works.

- Never pull the trigger of a gun to check if it is loaded or to release the action lock.
- Always point the muzzle of a gun in a safe direction when checking it.
- Do not allow any gun, including an air gun, to be used as a toy.
- Insist on safety rules being followed at all times by all members of the family.
- Learn how to operate all the guns in your home correctly, so you can handle them safely at any time.
- Encourage the shooting members of your family to participate in a hunter safety training course.
- If you have children who are interested in guns and shooting, give them an opportunity to learn proper gun handling, and to enjoy target shooting, through membership in a supervised shooting club.
- BB guns and children don't mix. One six-year study found that BB guns were the leading cause of serious eye injuries to children.

FIRE WORKS

Pyrotechnics (the art and science of fireworks) is a tradition so ancient its precise origin is unknown. Now a popular amusement worldwide, often associated with political or religious celebrations, fireworks are noisy, spectacular -- and powerful.

Treated with care, they can be the highlight of a festive occasion. But if not handled properly, they pose a serious threat to the safety of both those handling them and those watching nearby.

SAFETY SENSE

- Read the manufacturers' instructions for all pieces before beginning the display.
- Make sure your firing area is clean; remove any combustible items.
- Ensure that someone -- a single adult -- has overall responsibility for the display.
- Never allow young children to have firecrackers. Sparklers are fairly safe, but should not be used while other pieces are being set off.
- Carefully supervise older children around fireworks, and be sure they know the appropriate safety rules.
- Use two firing bases, such as buckets or wheelbarrows, filled with sand or earth.
- Ensure that long items, such as roman candles, are buried deep (halfway) in the sand.
- Keep a container of water or a hose

available and use it to soak smoldering pieces.
- Use a barbecue lighter with long handles to ignite pieces. Hold them at arm's length, ignite the wick, and stand back immediately.
- If a piece does not go off, do not try to relight it. Soak it with water and place it in the trash can.
- Set off firecrackers only on private property.
- Keep firecrackers out of your pockets.
- Do not allow anyone to play with firecrackers. They are not toys.
- Never throw firecrackers in the direction of people, animals, or buildings.
- Set off firecrackers in the open, not in bottles or other containers.
- Never flare or split firecrackers apart.
- Never leave your display until all fired goods have been disposed of in a metal trash container.

GARAGES

Every year we hear of a child being killed or injured by an automatic garage door as a result of children playing with the garage door openers. Youngsters make a game of activating the open door with the wall-mounted or remote control switch, then racing out of or into the garage to "beat" the door before it closes. Sometimes the child loses -- in every sense of the word. If the descending door strikes the child, it often pins the victim to the ground. Even doors having an automatic reverse feature have been involved in deaths.

SAFETY SENSE

• Forbid youngsters from playing in the garage unless there is adult supervision at all times.

• Ensure that the wall mount is out of reach of children. A protective box around it can prevent children from using a stick to activate it.

• Lock the remote control up in the car either by placing it in the (locked) glove box or locking the vehicle doors.

• Inspect both powered and manually operated garage doors regularly to be sure they are in safe operating condition.

• If installing an automatic door, do so in strict accordance with the manufacturer's instructions, and make a number of trial runs to ensure it is operating properly.

• Do not let children be the operators of the remote control. What is a fun thing to do today may result in a serious accident the next day.

• Always leave your garage door closed. This protects the contents of your garage and helps ensure that children will not play with the door.

• If you install an electric mechanism, remove the pull-down ropes used for manual operation.

• Leave your garage door lock in the open position. A good electric mechanism acts as a lock itself.

• Ensure that all partitions between an attached garage and the house are fire-resistant, and that any connecting doors are self-closing and raised above floor.

• Store combustible products in safety-approved containers.

• Never run the vehicle engine in a garage. Carbon monoxide can seep into other areas of the home and kill you.

GARAGE SALE BARGAINS

The price may be right -- but is it safe? Tools and appliances bought at garage sales come without warranties or service manuals. The phrase "buyer beware" should be on your mind constantly when shopping at garage sales. When shopping, follow these safety sense rules.

SAFETY SENSE

- Look for hidden defects like concealed corrosion on inside seams of pump-up tank sprayers, or ladders with split wood that has been painted over.
- Remember that an electric tool may work when the third-wire grounding plug has been snipped off, but the tool is hazardous.
- Be aware that older storm and shower doors may not have the safety glazing that is now available.
- Check old cribs that may have dangerous, wide-spaced slats and unreliable side latches.
- Old lamps featuring bulb sockets made of brass can be lethal. The insulation may rot away over time, thus creating the possibility of the socket becoming a shock hazard.
- Brass pull chains on old lamps can

be hazardous. These older lamps were often made without insulation.
- Take all used electrical appliances to an electrical store for a safety check.
- Replace plugs or prongs lacking insulation or protective covering.
- Inspect any electrical cord that has repair tape on it before using it.
- Used child car seats often come without all the vital equipment. A missing tether strap or missing bolts makes it impossible to anchor a car seat safely in your car.
- Ensure that eyes or other buttonlike decorations on children's toys are sewn on; otherwise they can be easily removed and swallowed.
- Used car tires are often structurally unsafe, so stay away from buying them.

GLASS HOMES

Panoramic views are characteristic of much of the architecture found in homes today. It's no wonder they are popular; they provide the best of two worlds -- outside beauty and inside comfort. But the trend to indoor-outdoor living presents a gloomy picture as far as safety is concerned. The culprit is the invisible glass door.

While glass doors bring the beauty of the outdoors into the home, they can also bring tragedy. People who live in glass houses are all too likely to walk right through the glass. If they are lucky, they may get off with skin cuts and a good scare. Others, unfortunately, suffer injuries serious enough to cause death, or scarring for life.

SAFETY SENSE

- Use skid-proof mats on the bathroom floor and keep the floor dry. Serious injuries often result when a person slips and then falls against a glass shower door or tub enclosure.
- People crash through glass doors because they don't see the glass. To make it visible, place decals (decorative stickers) or pressure tape on the glass at two levels: the adult's eye level and the child's eye level. (Decorative decals and pressure tape are available at nominal cost in most department, hardware, and variety stores).
- Many people have been injured by walking through the fixed glass panel next to a sliding door. To prevent a glass panel from being mistaken for an open door, use decals or pressure tape, or place a fairly tall potted plant or planter in front of it.
- Never assume that a glass door is open -- BE SURE! The last person through may have closed the door you opened just a minute before.
- Be equally sure you're going through the open door and not the fixed glass panel next to it.
- Children should be trained not to play near glass doors. Children at play forget to watch for danger, and may suffer serious injury if they run or are pushed through a glass door.
- Safety bars (also called muntin bars) can prevent actual contact with glass surfaces. They should be mounted at doorhandle level on a glass door that slides inside the fixed glass panel, and used on both sides of swinging doors. Safety bars are generally available through glass dealers.
- Scatter rugs, toys, and other articles that may cause people to slip, trip, or fall should be cleared from glass door areas.
- Check doorways frequently to be sure they remain clear.

HALLOWEEN

The peculiar customs of Halloween can make this holiday an especially enjoyable one, but they also pose hazards. The responsibility for making Halloween safe lies with both adults and children. Adhere to these tips to be sure the only scares you receive on this night are in fun.

SAFETY SENSE

- Keep your porch and yard light on.
- Do not leave breakables or obstacles (tools, ladders, children's playthings) on steps, lawns, or porches.
- Don't invite youngsters inside for treats; they have probably been given instructions not to go into other people's homes.
- Encourage trick-or-treating in the hours before darkness. Set hours for collections.
- Instruct children to use sidewalks and not walk in the street except at crosswalks or intersections. Remind them not to run between parked cars, across yards, or through empty lots.
- Insist that children bring their goodies home before eating them. Look over all treats before allowing children to eat them.
- Ensure competent supervision for all trick-or-treaters, according to the age and maturity of the child.
- Have all children carry a flashlight.
- Children should not go into a house or apartment unless the adult accompanying them gives approval.
- Choose a costume that is light in color so it can be seen at night. Use reflective tapes or bands.

- Be sure the costume flameproof; paper costumes should be fire-resistant.
- Check that the costume -- including any part such as a cape -- is the right length so that it will not trip a child.
- Be sure the costume allows freedom of movement -- no billowy or streaming parts to catch on bushes, hedges, or fences.
- Tie hats securely so that they will not slip.
- Use make-up instead of a mask, which may obscure vision.
- Ensure that whiskers, beards, wigs, veils, or hat trimmings do not obscure vision or cause a fire hazard.
- Include well-fitted shoes in a costume for ease in walking and running. Heavy boots, high heeled shoes, or dangling strings may trip a child.
- Do not allow candles or torches. Pumpkins or lanterns should be lit by flashlights.
- Don't let children carry a knife, sword, or other sharp instrument, even a make-believe one. They could be hurt in a fall or could accidentally hurt someone else.

HOME FIRE EXTINGUISHERS

A home fire extinguisher gives you valuable extra protection from grease fires or other small fires. Today's fire extinguishers are lightweight, uncomplicated, and inexpensive. If you don't have one in the kitchen -- and any-where else the risk is high, such as near a fireplace -- why not do some-thing about it?

A Class ABC fire extinguisher is the best buy for the home. Grease fires are Class B (flammable liquid) fires. But other kinds of fires could develop in the kitchen, or a grease fire could spread to another material. An all-purpose fire extinguisher can handle Class A (ordinary flammables -- paper, upholstery, and such) and Class C (electrical) fires as well as Class B.

SAFETY SENSE

• Mount your fire extinguisher in a wall bracket near the kitchen door. Don't put it near the stove or other place where a fire would be likely to block your reach.

• Always fight a fire with your back to the door so you'll be able to escape if the fire gets out of control.

• Use judgement about fighting a fire. If it's already severe or spreading, don't waste time trying to control it. Home fire extinguishers are very effective at combating small fires such as those in a wastebasket or stove, but they simply are not made for putting out large fires.

• If you decide you can't fight the fire (and don't hesitate to make that decision if you're not certain that you can put it out quickly), get everyone out of the house. Close the door behind you to slow the spread of smoke and fire. When that's done, call the fire department from a neighbor's home.

• Try to attend a community fire safety course. They are often sponsored by local fire departments. They will explain and demonstrate how to extinguish small fires.

• Have extinguishers inspected and recharged at least annually.

• After an extinguisher is used, replace or refill it immediately. Don't wait.

INSIDE AIR POLLUTION

If you think housework is killing you, you may be right. Your home could be harboring potentially dangerous pollutants that can trigger allergic reactions, or even contribute to causing cancer.

In very tight or energy efficient homes indoor pollutants can build up to unacceptable levels if not removed. As people try to save energy by adding sealing and weatherstripping to their homes, they are also trapping unwanted pollutants inside. A ventilation system is the main way of removing pollutants from the home.

These indoor air pollutants include: benzene from soiled clothing or storage gas cans; tetrachlorothylene from dry-cleaned materials; asbestos (in older model homes); radon gas (a natural by-product of the decay of uranium and thorium in the earth); carbon monoxide, which can spill from combustion appliances; formaldehyde gas, which can seep from the resins in particle board and plywood panelling; methylene chloride (from paint and paint thinners); tricloroethane, an ingredient in some aerosol sprays and mold and mildew, which can cause allergic reactions and illness (in the case of some molds).

SAFETY SENSE

- Be sure your house is adequately ventilated, including the basement. This will keep down the levels of indoor pollutants.
- Follow manufacturers' directions when using products that emit pollutants.
- Use the proper protective equipment.
- If working with dangerous substances, be sure your work space is very well ventilated -- opening a window may not be adequate to work safely with some products. Install an exhaust fan or, if possible, move the project outside. Note whether the product should be kept away from heat sources.
- Keep paints and cleaning solvents in the original, tightly-sealed containers and store them in cool, well-vented areas. Discard partially-empty containers unless you're sure you'll use the rest of the product soon.
- Clean air conditioners, air ducts, air filters, heat exchangers and humidifiers regularly. They are all potential sources of allergens or disease-producing organisms.
- If you have gas appliances, check them regularly to make sure the pilot lights are burning with a clear blue flame. Burning gas produces small amounts of carbon monoxide and, when the pilots aren't burning cleanly, they give off even more pollutants. If these accidently spread throughout the home, they can have adverse effects on your health. If you're buying new gas appliances, consider ones with spark ignition systems, which eliminate the need for pilot lights.

LADDERS

Would you jump out of a plane without knowing how to skydive? Of course not. Before taking your chances falling through space, you would want to be certain you knew how to handle a parachute.

Yet every day, thousands of people risk falling through space in what could be a fatal accident by ignoring ladder safety rules.

Most ladder accidents could be avoided if users would make certain of two things: that the ladder is secured against movement, and that it is placed at the proper angle.

The better a ladder is secured, the more stable it is. Obviously, a ladder that sits on a level, firm place and is tied at the top becomes a more dependable stairway.

A ladder placed at the proper angle will give the user the most dependable support. A ladder that is too vertical can topple backward, while one that is too horizontal can fall under the weight of the user. The correct angle is about 75 degrees (a four-to-one ratio). You can estimate this with an old fire fighters' rule of thumb: Stand erect with your toes at the ladder feet; if you hold the ladder by the side rails with your arms extended horizontally, the ladder will be at approximately the right angle.

SAFETY SENSE

- Use only ladders that are sturdy and well built.
- Buy straight or extension ladders that have non-slip feet, quality side rails, rungs, and steps, and thick rubber treads. The braces on a stepladder should not twist or wobble when standing on it. You should be able to raise or lower the sections of extension ladders smoothly.
- Keep your ladder in good condition.
- Always be sure that an extension ladder is right side up.
- Secure the footings properly.
- Always open a stepladder fully, and make sure it is stable before climbing on it.
- Never stand on the top cap (step) of a stepladder.
- Never reach too far while on a ladder; you may lose your balance.
- Inspect a ladder before using it; is it stable?
- Don't use a ladder if you have taken medication, alcohol, or are generally not feeling well.
- If working near electrical wires or installations, use a ladder made of non-conductive material.

LATCHKEY CHILDREN

Thousands of children every day return home from school to an empty house with parent(s) or guardian still at work. The number of such children -- nicknamed "latchkey" kids because they carry a housekey, often on a string or chain worn around their neck -- is growing in our society. If your family has children who return home by themselves after school, insist that they learn and follow sensible safety rules:

SAFETY SENSE

For Parents:

- Make it clear what time you or other family members are arriving, either early or late, and give instructions on what to do in case you do not arrive when expected.
- Leave a list of all emergency numbers near the telephone, including the numbers of parents, relatives, neighbors, and friends. Make sure that your children know exactly who to call for each kind of emergency.
- Instruct your children on how to answer calls, so they will be comfortable when the telephone rings.
- Keep a well-charged flashlight in a place your children can find easily in case of power failure.
- Make sure there is alternative shelter for children in case they cannot get into the home.
- Instruct your children on the basics of handling a household emergency: how to turn off the main electrical switch, the water and gas valves, etc.
- Enroll youngsters in a basic first-aid course in case of injury to themselves or younger children in their care.
- Leave prepared after-school food snacks so children will not have to use electrical appliances, stoves, or other potentially dangerous equipment.

For Children:

- Do not talk to strangers. If ignored, the stranger is likely to leave you alone.
- Never enter your home when there is a possibility of danger inside.
- If someone rings the doorbell, do not say that you are home alone. Just tell the person at the door that you are not interested. If your parents prefer that you not answer the door when you are alone, stick to it. If someone persists in trying to get into the house, call the police.
- Learn how to answer the telephone politely and safely. If someone is looking for your parents, take a message. Tell the caller that they can't come to the phone rather than saying that you are home alone.
- Keep your house keys in a safe and inconspicuous place. Keys carried around your neck in plain view invite trouble.

LIFTING AND CARRYING

We don't really know how many people hurt their backs every year because many incidents are never reported. Major back injuries from lifting get most of the attention because they translate into time off work, but this doesn't mean we should ignore the minor aches and pains. Even if slight pulls don't result in time off work, they can still hurt for a long time.

Proper methods of lifting and handling protect against injury and also make the job easier. Wear gloves and safety shoes for jobs involving the handling of heavy materials. When equipment is available and conditions make it practical, use mechanical devices, such as dollies, carts, and wagons, for lifting and carrying.

SAFETY SENSE

- Size up the load and check the overall conditions before lifting. Do not try to lift a load alone if it appears too heavy or awkward. Check that there is adequate space for movement and good footing.
- Look for slivers, nails, sharp ends, etc., when handling materials or packages. If possible, remove them.
- Make certain that you have good balance. Place your feet shoulder-width apart, one foot beside and the

other foot behind the item to lifted.
- Bend your knees; do not stoop. Keep your back straight. Tucking in the chin straightens the back.
- Grip the load with the palms of your hands and with your fingers for security.
- Use your body weight to start the load moving and then lift by pushing up with your legs. This is your strongest set of muscles -- make use of it.

MATCHES AND LIGHTERS

About six percent of fire deaths can be attributed to the unsafe use of matches and lighters. Most fires start as a result of children playing with matches and lighters, matches which are disposed of unsafely or rubbish being ignited inadvertently.

SAFETY SENSE

- Always keep matches and lighters out of the reach of young children. Supervise older children closely until they have learned to use such items safely.
- Seek professional help if your child persistently plays with matches. The chances of pyromania are slight, but an unusual interest in matches may reflect some emotional problem that needs treatment, not punishment.
- Never carry "strike-anywhere" matches loose in the pockets of clothing; they may ignite if accidentally hit.
- Remove only one match at a time from the container. Several matches bunched together may flash and cause serious hand burns.
- Close the box or folder before striking a match to prevent the other matches from igniting.
- Always strike a match away from the end of the box containing the heads of the other matches to lessen the danger of igniting in case there is a spark.
- Before opening a box of matches, check to be sure the box is right side up; spilled matches may be picked up later by children.
- Always strike matches away from yourself, but never toward anyone, since the head may fly off. Watch for sparks. Be careful not to strike the match (or light a lighter) close to anyone's face.
- Use long-handled matches when trying to light material that is difficult to reach, especially if parts of your clothing might be exposed to the flame.
- When lighting any gas appliance, always light the match before turning on the gas.
- Store matches in a tightly closed metal container when possible. If you put them in a stand, place the heads down so they will not accidentally

ignite.

- Use a flashlight or electric light, not a flame, when rummaging in a closet, attic, basement, or garage. There may be combustible materials around.
- Do not allow children to use match heads as a heat source in chemical experiments.
- Break burned stick matches in half to make sure that the flame is extinguished. If the match is too hot to break, it may still ignite and is, therefore, too hot to throw away.
- Never throw burned matches into wastebaskets or containers of combustible material. Do not throw them from automobiles or onto floors where infants might pick them up. Use proper ash receptacles, making sure first that no wads of paper have been placed there.
- If a match head flies off, or if the match breaks before the head is ig-

nited, take care to burn the match before throwing it away.
- Take care never to discard burned matches near leaves or grass. Many forest fires have been caused by people discarding matches that were not completely extinguished.
- Do not carry a butane lighter if you are planning to use either flame-cutting equipment or abrasive grinding/cutting equipment. Flames or hot sparks could rupture the butane container and cause serious injury.
- Never leave a lighter on the dashboard of a vehicle where sunlight could cause overheating and over-pressurization of the fluid in the container.
- Before putting a lighter back in a pocket or purse, be sure it is completely extinguished.
- Do not attempt to refill a lighter near a flame, an electric or gas stove, or any kind of heater.

MOBILE HOMES

Mobile homes provide shelter for millions of North Americans, allowing many families who otherwise would not have the means to own a home of their own. Today's mobile home parks and subdivisions are spacious and have many of the services of urban communities. Like all homes, they experience their share of accidents, and, in fact, some features of mobile homes make them more vulnerable to accidents than conventional homes. In some ways, however, mobile homes are often safer than other types of housing.

SAFETY SENSE

- Mobile homes are required to have smoke detectors installed, while conventional homes may not be. At least one detector placed near the ceiling at the living room end will provide sufficient warning.
- Be aware that mobile homes must meet certain flammability (rate of burning) requirements.
- Remember that mobile homes have a relatively light weight and are, therefore, more susceptible to high winds, especially of tornado or hurricane force.
- Equip your mobile home with "tie-down" or anchoring points -- and use them.
- If weather reports indicate high wind or warn of possible hurricanes or tornados, evacuate your home and go the nearest public shelter or to a neighbor's conventional home for protection.
- Position your home near a natural windbreak, such as a hill or a clump of trees.

PAINTING AND DECORATING

Painting and decorating safely requires that you select quality paints, know what type of wallpaper to use, choose reliable tools, and wear protective clothing for the job. Once you have made all the right decisions, observe the manufacturers' instructions for using the products.

Chemical paint stripping materials can be flammable, explosive, corrosive, and/or contain toxic vapors. This can cause burns, lung irritation, headaches, and nausea. Prolonged exposure may lead to cancer. To avoid these problems, wear gloves, mask, and protective clothing; keep containers closed and work in a ventilated area.

Paint stripping with a wire brush or by sanding can cause dust that may be toxic. Always wear a mask, eye protection, and gloves.

SAFETY SENSE

- Use latex paints for home projects whenever practical, since it is safest. It can be used as a primer or final coat and can be cleaned with water.
- If you must use oil-based paints, be careful. They have an offensive odor, and you may be allergic to the fungicide used in outside paints.
- Oil-based paints are also flammable, so that means no smoking and no fire sources in the vicinity.
- Eliminate paint fumes by supplying good ventilation: keep windows open.
- Never buy paints or solvents meant for commercial or industrial use. They often require special handling precautions.
- Avoid using lead-based paints in or around the home. If lead is swallowed by youngsters it can produce serious medical problems.
- Be aware that epoxies, sealers, lacquers, swimming pool paints, basement floor paints, special primers and urethane finishes all contain strong solvents and are flammable.
- Always follow the ventilation instructions for decorating products. Inhaling epoxies, lacquers, etc., can cause headaches, dizziness, drowsi-ness, nausea, blurred vision, and irritation of the eyes, nose, throat and lungs.
- Protect your vision by wearing safety glasses or goggles. The tiniest paint speck can harm eye tissue.
- Dress to cover your skin as much as possible when painting in order to prevent any allergic reactions or skin irritations.

213

- Leave spray painting to professionals. It involves special hazards, such as paint droplets being inhaled, paint being pressure-injected into skin from spraying, fire, explosion, and electrical shock.
- Use mineral spirits, varsol, or turpentine to clean oil-based paintbrushes. Never use gasoline.
- Store paints, thinners, and solvents in tightly sealed cans.
- Dispose of paint rags immediately in an outside location.
- When stripping furniture with solvents, read the product label and follow directions regarding protective equipment, ventilation, smoking, etc.

PARK PLAYGROUNDS

There is a wide variety of equipment available for public playgrounds today. Traditional slides, swings, and jungle gyms have been used and enjoyed for years, while recent trends toward innovative play spaces have inspired such unconventional equipment as railroad ties and tires.

If a public playground in your area is unsafe, report it to your parks and recreation department.

SAFETY SENSE

- Remove equipment from asphalt or concrete surfaces. These areas can be used for activities such as hopscotch or basketball.
- If removing equipment is not feasible, cover the areas under equipment with shock absorbent material (sand, etc.), especially around high slides or areas where children are likely to fall.
- If equipment is crowded together, consider moving some pieces to ease congestion.
- Do not hesitate to eliminate a piece of equipment that has been the site of frequent injuries.
- Check that equipment is firmly anchored in the ground by concrete, and that concrete footings are below ground level to prevent tripping.
- If any concrete footings are exposed, cover them with earth or padding. Recover worn surfaces where rocks or other hazards protrude.
- If swing sets are crowded, remove one or two swings. Add tire swings,

which permit safe use by several children at one time and have a better safety record. Drill holes in tires to ensure water drainage.
- Replace heavy swing seats with lightweight seats, such as canvas or plastic.
- Remove any obstructions between play units that a child might accidentally run into or trip over, such as wires or ropes. Where barriers are useful, such as between ball fields and playgrounds or between playgrounds and roadways, install solid fences or walls.
- Install or paint on slip-resistant surfaces on climbing and gripping components (handles, foot rests, etc.).
- Consider color-coding equipment for different age groups and posting explanatory signs in prominent locations.
- Use brightly colored paint or tape to make a potentially hazardous protru-

sion on a piece of equipment more visible.

- Provide clearly marked pathways and encourage children to keep to the paths rather than cutting through areas where swings, merry-go-rounds, etc., are in motion.
- Carefully inspect homemade equipment for splinters, rough edges, sharp corners, and loose or protruding nails, nuts, bolts, etc. Use cedar, redwood, or pressure treated lumber in areas where the wood comes in contact with soil, or in humid climates.
- Post emergency telephone numbers in a prominent location -- near a telephone, if one is available.
- Clean, inspect, and maintain playgrounds on a regular schedule. Watch for hazards such as broken glass or sharp metal objects.

PICNICKING

One thing that can make any kind of food taste twice as good is the great outdoors. Picnicking makes food taste great, and the things that go with it -- softball, swimming, or whatever you please -- are equally enjoyable.

But, as with most activities, there are hazards involved. Two things can spoil a picnic, or even a summer: getting sick and getting hurt. You can avoid both with some safety sense knowhow about food and fun outdoors.

SAFETY SENSE

- Know that food poisoning can result from eating food containing disease-producing bacteria. Some common examples are salmonella, dysentery organisms, and poisons produced by bacteria toxins such as staphylococcus. Dishes, such as potato salad, fruit salads with whipped cream, mayonnaise or milk, puddings and custards, white sauces, sandwich spreads, meat and fish salad sandwiches, are the most likely to harbor harmful bacteria.
- Most cold sandwiches should not be eaten if they have been unrefrigerated for more than four hours.
- Allow cooked food to cool in the container in which it was prepared, but do not handle again.
- Do not leave unrefrigerated, or uncovered for a long time in a car trunk or on a picnic table.
- Handle cold meats with a fork, not your fingers. Fingers spread germs.
- Eat a packed lunch that can't be

refrigerated within three hours.
- Use a lot of non-perishables like potato chips, raw fruits and vegetables, cheese, peanut butter, jam, and canned goods. These keep well and generally cause no problems.
- Do not allow charcoal briquettes to lie smouldering long after the food is cooked. Worse yet, do not dump and scatter them to burn an unsuspecting foot. Douse them with water when you're finished cooking.
- Wear shoes outdoors, and watch where you step. To be on the really safest side -- at picnics or anywhere else -- be sure you've had a tetanus shot.
- Never toss an empty can or bottle where someone might step on it.
- Don't get so absorbed in playing or preparing goodies that you take an eye off the younger members of the family, particularly toddlers.
- Learn to identify poison ivy, oak, and sumach and steer clear of them. The

rashes they cause usually aren't serious, but can create plenty of discomfort.

- If caught in an electrical storm, the safest place to be is in a car with the windows closed. The metal frame of the car dissipates the electrical forces into the ground.
- If you are caught in the open during a storm, look quickly for a ditch or depression and lie in it. But remember, if the ditch is a creek bed, it may suddenly fill with deep, running water.
- On picnic outings, as always, follow the cardinal rule for swimmers: never swim alone! Use the buddy system.
- Make sure there is lots of suntan lotion available, and limit the amount of sun exposure time.
- Be prepared for the heat. Wear light-colored clothing, which reflects heat and helps your body maintain normal temperature. Top it off with a hat. While your body is filling up on sun, fill it up on water to prevent dehydration.
- Drive safely going home from the picnic so you'll be around to go on another. If you've been drinking, don't drive.

PLANT DANGERS

Most everyone has plants in the home or the garden, although many people don't really know much about them. Some plants, although beautiful, can be extremely dangerous if eaten. Some young children are prone to eating plants, so keep house plants out of reach of children, and teach them not to eat any part of plants. In the garden, uproot any plant you suspect is poisonous and burn it. Respect all wild plants, especially poison ivy, hemlock, and mushrooms. The following chart can help you clear your home, green-house or garden of poisonous plants.

SAFETY SENSE

PLANT	SYMPTOMS
VEGETABLES	
Rhubarb	Large amounts of leaves can cause nausea, vomiting, weakness, muscle cramps, and kidney damage.
Daphne	Local irritation around mouth, nausea, vomiting, diarrhea. A few berries may kill a child.
Golden Chain	Nausea, vomiting, pallor, drowsiness. With severe poisoning, excitement, staggering, convulsions, coma. May be fatal if eaten in sufficient quantity.
Laurels	Burning in mouth, nausea, vomiting, depression, breathing difficulties, prostration. In extreme cases, coma and death.
Rhododendrons	Burning in mouth, nausea, vomiting, depression, breathing difficulties, prostration. In extreme cases, coma and death.
Jasmine (Azaleas)	Digestive disturbances, sweating, nervousness.
WILD PLANTS	
Buttercups	Juices may severely irritate the digestive system.

PLANT	SYMPTOMS
Nightshade	Intense digestive disturbances and nervousness. There are several types, of which Deadly Nightshade is the most toxic and may be fatal.
Poison Hemlock	Extremely poisonous. Vomiting, loss of muscle control.
Poison Ivy	Mild poisoning results in a rash. Serious cases may result in acute discomfort. Eating any part of the plant is dangerous.
HOUSE PLANTS	
Oleander	Affects heart; produces severe digestive upset. Has been known to be fatal.
Poinsettia	Sap produces vomiting and diarrhea.
Dieffenbachia	Burning and irritation of mouth and tongue. Can be fatal if back of tongue swells enough to block air passages.
Mistletoe	Can cause irritation of digestive tract with vomiting, diarrhea and abdominal pain. May also cause high blood pressure.
FLOWER GARDEN	
Lily-of-the-valley	Irregular heart beat and pulse, usually accompanied by digestive upset and mental confusion.
Foxglove	A source of the drug digitalis, used to stimulate the heart. In large amounts, causes dangerously irregular heartbeat and pulse, digestive upset, and mental confusion. May be fatal.
Bleeding Heart	May be poisonous in large amounts. Has proved fatal to cattle.

POISON-PROOF YOUR HOME

We live in an age of chemicals. Hundreds of them have become part of our lifestyle, making our lives easier in various ways. However, many of the drugs, medications, cleansers, petroleum products, insecticides, etc., that have become common household items are potentially dangerous, particularly to young children.

As we use more and more toxic medicines and household and industrial poisons, our children become more likely to encounter them. Today's average North American household has as many poisons in the form of detergents, bleaches, birth control pills, insecticides, polishes, solvents, A.S.A., disinfectants, etc. They're in every part of the house, from the bathroom to the kitchen to the living room, in the basement, the garage, the car, the closets, and the drawers. In many of these places, they can be reached by small children, who love to explore, climb, and swallow. Small children are the highest risk group for accidental poisoning.

SAFETY SENSE

- Don't put medicines with other household products. Keep them in their original containers, never in cups, bowls, or soft-drink containers. Lock them up.
- Do not suggest to children that medicine tastes like candy. Keep vitamin and iron tablets, which look like candy, locked up.
- Be certain all bottles, cans, and containers are properly labelled.
- Use a prescription drug only for the person for whom it is intended. Keep prescription drugs locked up.
- Avoid taking medicine in a child's presence; children tend to imitate adults.
- Clean out the medicine cabinet regularly. Consult your poison control center or doctor on safe disposal of old medications.
- Advise all family members of poten-

tial dangers when using insect repellents, weed killers, lye, solvents, paint thinners, or cleaning agents.
- Move all dangerous household plants to a safe place, perhaps hanging from the ceiling. Teach your children from an early age never to eat plants or berries.
- Don't leave purses lying around. Put them out of harm's way, and encourage your guests to do the same thing.
- Periodically check your house, room by room, for poisons. Put all potentially dangerous items in a safe place, then use a location sticker to remind the household that a particular area contains hazardous substances.
- Keep the telephone number of your poison information center and/or hospital emergency department close at hand.

SAFEGUARDING THE ELDERLY

Although families with small children often take great care to see that their homes are as safe and convenient as possible for youngsters, installing every latest device to reduce hazards, many people seem to feel such care serves no purpose in a family of adults. But are such measures and devices really no longer needed in our households? What about Mother, or Dad? Uncle Harry, Aunt Clara, or Grandpa? Are they as spry and agile as they once were, or could they also benefit from similar devices to make life a little easier for them and keep them safer?

Listed below are just a few of the things that can be done to make life safer for the elderly in our homes.

SAFETY SENSE

• Never store medicines, cleaning agents, or pesticides near food and spices.

• Prepare special medicine labels with extra-large letters for those with poor eye sight.

• Always pour medicines from the side opposite the label to keep the label clear to read.

• Paste or glue bits of sandpaper on the bottles and caps of medicines that are not to be taken internally. People with poor eye sight will feel the cap difference.

• Store internal medicines separately from external medicines. For extra protection, draw a large red X on external medicine labels.

• Measure out only one night's supply of pills at a time. Keep a light handy on the nightstand to avoid errors in taking medication.

• Provide enough light switches so that

people do not have to grope through dark rooms, halls, or stairways.

• Provide sturdy handrails on both sides.

• Provide strategically-placed grab bars in the bathroom near tub and shower.

• Adjust the heights of beds and chairs to make them easy to get into and out of.

• Encourage those who walk unsteadily to wear well-fitting shoes and clothing that doesn't dangle or trail.

• Supply storage that can be easily reached by everyone (between hip and eye level).

• Remove slipping and tripping hazards, such as toys, throw rugs, and low furniture, from all traffic areas. Wipe up spills and pick up objects immediately.

• Call attention to any new furniture arrangements.

• Have a place for everything and keep

everything in its place.

- Mark the control settings for kitchen ranges in large letters for easy reading.
- Make sure that the gas range has an automatic pilot light for the oven as well as the burners.
- Choose electric appliances with indicator pilot lights that shine when the unit is on.
- Bring electrical wiring up to date by repairing or replacing any frayed or broken appliance cords and plugs, and by adding enough outlets to handle your electrical loads safely.
- Install guards or screens on heating devices that might come in contact with parts of the body.
- Discourage the wearing of loose, flimsy garments around sources of flame or heat, such as kitchen ranges, fireplaces, and space heaters.
- Select cooking utensils that are lightweight, with flat bottoms and insulated handles.
- Insist on a "no smoking while lying down" rule for everyone in the house.
- Provide large, deep ashtrays for smokers.
- Provide and point out easy escape routes in the event of fire.

SMOKE DETECTORS

It only takes a few minutes for a spark to become a destructive fire. Smoke detectors can save lives by sounding an alarm in the early stages of a fire, allowing time for people to safely leave the dwelling. However, using detectors does not eliminate the need for regular fire hazard inspections, handy fire extinguishers, and carefully prepared escape routes.

Smoke detectors work in two different ways. A photoelectric smoke detector sends forth a beam of light from a photoelectric bulb. When smoke particles are in the air, they reflect the light from the beam into a photocell, and the alarm is triggered. This type of detector works best for detecting smouldering fires, such as those started by a burning cigarette left on a mattress or an upholstered chair. A pilot light will blink off, and a buzz or hail will sound in photoelectric models when a bulb is burned out.

An ionization chamber smoke detector produces electrically-charged air molecules called ions, which create a small electric current in the chamber. (The radioactive material in the ionization chamber is not hazardous.) Any smoke particles that enter the chamber attach themselves to these ions, reducing the flow of the current and setting off the alarm. An ionization chamber detector is best for sensing the presence of flaming fires with little visible smoke.

SAFETY SENSE

- Do not purchase a detector unless it bears the label of an authorized testing agency, e.g., CSA or UL.
- Place detectors in all rooms, or at least between living and sleeping areas. Some 60 percent of home fires occur between 10 p.m. and 6 a.m.
- In multi-storied houses, also place detectors on the ceilings of stairwells to separate the floor levels.
- Place smoke detectors on or near the ceiling, away from doors and other obstructions. Do not place detectors on ceilings of an uninsulated attic or in a mobile home. Place it on the side wall, 15 to 30 cm (6 to 12 in.) below the ceiling.
- Although not very practical, for increased protection, keep bedroom doors closed at night, providing an additional smoke barrier.
- Install interconnected units for added safety. When one unit detects smoke, all detectors will sound an alarm.

- Read maintenance instructions for routine service of smoke detector.
- Test detectors regularly as recommended by the manufacturer; establish a date for these tests ahead of time and mark it on your calendar.
- Clean filters on photoelectric units regularly (at least once a year).
- Change batteries as required. Battery-powered models will beep or flash a light for a week or more to indicate that their batteries are weak. Detectors powered by household electric current should also give a warning signal when not working.
- If you go away, advise your neighbors of the sound of your alarm -- it may save your home. On your return, check that the battery has not lost power.

SOLVENTS, FLAMMABLE AND COMBUSTIBLE LIQUIDS

A flammable or combustible liquid will catch fire and burn. Many commonly used solvents, waxes, cleaners, adhesives, thinners, and polishes are flammable or combustible. Common ignition sources are hot surfaces, open flames, hot particles, and sparks.

SAFETY SENSE

- Use only containers bearing an approved agency's safety label for storing solvents or other flammable and combustible liquids.
- Never store fuels in glass bottles, open vessels, or other unapproved containers. Only approved containers are suitable to withstand pressure build-up.
- Keep plastic and metal cans in good repair with all screw caps in place. Discard them if damaged or leaking.
- Use only the caps supplied by the manufacturer; a badly fitting cap will allow vapor and possibly liquid to escape. Never use a rag or other makeshift plug, because the material can act as a wick to draw up liquids.
- Be sure that every container has the common name of the product printed on the side in a contrasting color in letters at least 8 cm (3 in.) high. Appearance and smell are not relia-

ble for determining what is in the container.
- Never sniff an unknown liquid to try to find out what it is; serious health problems may result.
- If you absolutely must change the contents of a container, make sure it is completely empty before filling it with the new product. Attach a large tag with the name of the new contents.
- Never fill a container beyond the full mark. The mark is calculated to leave a five percent air space for fuel expansion in rising temperatures.
- If the container is a metal drum or tank, beware of the increased hazard presented by storing and transporting larger quantities of volatile liquids.
- Select a drum or tank approved for the product.
- Have all traces of previous contents professionally removed to avoid

contamination.

- When transporting portable fuel containers, stow them securely in an upright position, clear of any heat source (such as the exhaust system of the vehicle) and of any sharp objects that may cause a puncture or other damage.
- Never use open containers, buckets, cans, tanks, or drums for flammable and combustible liquids.
- Never smoke around flammable and combustible liquids.

- Dispose flammable or combustible materials according to instructions on the container.
- Avoid skin contact: wear appropriate protective equipment, such as, gloves, creams, aprons, etc.
- Don't breath the vapors: if the area is not well-ventilated, use an approved respirator.
- Protect your eyes: always wear safety glasses, goggles, or a face shield when handling hazardous materials.

SPACE HEATERS

It can be a fatal mistake to use a kerosene heater in your bedroom or any small room while you sleep. Yet some people do so, and may even compound the danger by closing the door and windows. These units can produce carbon monoxide, a very deadly gas. When buying any space heater, be sure that it has been safety-certified by a recognized agency and use it in accordance with the manu-facturers' instructions.

SAFETY SENSE

- Ensure that electric space heaters are properly grounded and that the cord plug has three prongs.
- Keep electric space heaters away from upholstery, curtains, and other burnable items.
- Be sure that electric heaters have a safety switch that turns the heater off if it is tipped over.
- Never use kerosene heaters in poorly ventilated areas or leave them burn-ing unattended. If the unit malfunc-tions, it can produce poisonous carbon monoxide. There is also danger of fire if the appliance isn't functioning properly.
- If you have a kerosene heater, refer regularly to the manufacturer's in-structions for operation and mainte-nance until you are totally familiar with it.
- Carry out maintenance procedures at required intervals and carefully follow

step-by-step refuelling instructions.
- Use only K1 grade kerosene. Poorer grades can leave deposits that may contribute to the production of carbon monoxide in malfunctioning heaters.
- When buying or storing kerosene, put it in a fuel container designed for that purpose.
- Buy kerosene in the smallest quanti-ties practical to avoid storing exces-sive amounts of fuel.
- Do not pour kerosene down drains or sewers or onto the ground. If your municipality holds toxic household waste disposal days, throw contain-ers or unneeded kerosene away then.
- Never store kerosene in or beside a house.
- Do not refuel a kerosene heater inside. Warn children to stay away from kerosene heaters and fuels of all types.

SPRAY CANS

From deodorants and cosmetics to paints, cleansers, polishes, and sanitizers, many products are packaged in convenient aerosol containers. Such containers are generally safe -- they only cause accidents when the product or its package are misused. Read the label on the aerosol cans for directions on proper use and storage.

SAFETY SENSE

- Keep aerosols away from sources of heat, such as stoves, radiators, or sunlight. When an aerosol container is heated, the pressure generated by the vaporization of the liquid propellant that is used to spray the contents builds up quickly until the container cannot hold it in any longer. An explosion may result.
- Be especially careful when disposing of aerosol containers. If a can is tossed into a fire, or heated in any other way, the result may be an explosion and the violent projection of container parts.
- Beware of puncturing aerosol containers. This releases the contents in an uncontrolled way.
- Avoid breathing in the spray from an aerosol container. Prevent contact with eyes, nose, ears, and mouth. While present evidence has not shown there to be any danger for a person using aerosol products according to instructions, problems from inhalation are still the subject of research.
- Remember that safe use of aerosols will avoid most dangers. Make sure that they aren't used as toys.
- Never inhale aerosols intentionally to try to reach an intoxicated state, and be sure your children understand that this can be fatal.
- Avoid letting spray fallout drift into your eyes. Eyes are naturally sensitive to airborne aerosol droplets. Check the direction of the spray valve each time before use.

TURNING OFF TROUBLE

The dictionary defines an emergency as "an unforseen happening requiring prompt action." We might add that many minor household emergencies can quickly become major ones when people don't know what "prompt action" to take.

Household emergencies often involve gas, water, and/or electricity. Even if you have no desire to join the ranks of the do-it-yourselfer, you should know how to handle a utility emergency in your home. Standing ankle-deep in water is not the time to realize you don't know how to stop the flood.

SAFETY SENSE

WATER

- Find the main water shut-off valve in your home. If a pipe bursts or toilet tank cracks, water will flow at full pressure until someone turns it off. The main shut-off tap handle is usually fairly large and is often painted blue.
- In a single-family home, the shut-off will usually be in the basement, near where the water service enters the building, or near the water meter. In homes without basements, the water shutoff may be under the kitchen sink, near the water heater, or in a utility room or bathroom closet.
- Once you have located the main water shut-off, hang a large tag on it.
- Make sure the shut-off is working. Shut-offs are used so seldom that they may become "frozen" in the open position. To help loosen it, spray the stem with a penetrating lubricant or use a pair of pliers.

- Find the shut-off for the water heater. If the water heater springs a leak, you can turn off the hot water in the house, but still use the cold water at the toilets and sinks.

GAS

- Any time you smell gas, find out what's wrong.
- Check first to see if a pilot light has been extinguished. If so, relight it.
- If the smell is not from a pilot, get everyone out of the house, open windows and doors, and don't use any electrical equipment, such as fans or lights. Call the gas company (from a neighbor's house if your phone is in the same area as the gas odor). If the meter is not located near the smell, turn off the gas.
- Know where your gas shut-off is. Look for a square or rectangular short rod protruding from the pipe leading

to the meter. You will need a wrench, preferably adjustable, to operate it. Don't practice on this shut-off. If you ever have to turn off the gas, don't attempt repairs yourself, and don't turn it back on yourself.

ELECTRICITY

- If a light switch starts to smoke or the electric range begins to shoot sparks, turn off all the power to the house unless you can quickly identify the specific circuit that is the culprit.
- Know the location of the service panel, which is the heart of the electrical system, and the location of the main shut-off. It may be behind a small metal door in the kitchen or hall, or it may consist of one or more metal boxes in the basement or garage.
- Be aware that service panels vary greatly. There may not be one main control, in which case you will have to unscrew all the individual fuses, remove a main fuse, or snap off all the circuit breakers in an emergency.
- Any time you open your service panel, make certain you are standing on a dry surface and use only one hand. Don't touch with your free hand any other grounded object, such as another electric service panel or a water pipe.
- Keep a good flashlight available near the service panel for emergency power failure.
- Keep a list of telephone numbers for service companies handy. Unless you are an experienced do-it-yourselfer, you will need the services of a plumber or electrician or your gas company after you have shut down the water, gas, or electrical system.

WINDOWS AND BALCONIES

Each year, a number of lives are lost through falls from windows and balconies. The majority of victims are very young children. These accidents often occur when the child climbs up to look out of a window, or over a railing, or to retrieve a toy. Adults may fall while cleaning the outside of a window.

SAFETY SENSE

- Be sure that all balconies and other railings have a minimum height of 106 cm (42 in.).
- Avoid horizontal railing or openings which could provide a foothold and encourage a child to climb. Instead, use railings that are solid or consist of vertical rods with a space no more than 9 cm (3 1/2 in.) between openings.
- The balcony handrail or top of the railing should not be more that 5 cm (2 in.) wide and should be sloped or rounded. This removes the tempta- tion to sit on it or to place on it flower pots or other objects that might fall and injure people below.
- Install an upstand or toe board on a balcony to prevent balls or other toys from falling through, thus eliminating the danger of a child's climbing up to try to retrieve them.
- Check that your balcony drains water clear of other balconies at a lower level.
- On upper-story windows, particularly in the baby's bedroom, install window guards that permit only a 7.6 to 10 cm (3 to 4 in.) opening. Don't count on the screen to keep a child safely inside. Falls from windows are often fatal.
- Keep furniture away from windows. Children will often climb up to look out the window and accidentally fall through the screen.
- Put a safety latch on windows that only adults can open.
- Do not sit or lean out a window to clean it. Clean from the outside or remove the window from the inside and clean it.

WINTERIZING YOUR HOME

Many home accidents happen because residents are caught unaware -- or unprepared. Winter brings on more such surprises than any other season. Falls, fires, and poisonings result from disorder and neglect, as well as a simple lack of knowledge as to what should be done to make a home ready for winter.

SAFETY SENSE

- Store pesticides in their original, labelled containers.
- Dispose of empty pesticide containers so they pose no hazards to humans or animals.
- Store pesticides out of reach of children, pets, or irresponsible people.
- Wash spray equipment and put it away for the season.
- Remove all combustibles from the vicinity of heat.
- If you burn rubbish, use a special container.
- Remove rubbish from basement, attic, garage, and closets.
- Keep oily rags in metal containers.
- Check ladders to make sure they are in good condition.
- Be sure you know how to brace a ladder to keep it from slipping, as well as other basic ladder safety rules. See page 207 in Specialty Topics section.
- Keep the furnace and flue in good repair and free of combustibles.
- Ensure proper ventilation for the heating system(s).
- Change furnace filters regularly. If there is a blower, have it cleaned and oiled.

- Have the fireplace inspected for loose mortar.
- Be sure the fireplace opening is screened.
- Drain the swimming pool and cover it. Put water treating chemicals away safely. Lock up all outside entrances to the pool.
- Be sure all pool electrical equipment has been disconnected.
- Be sure there is ample light outdoors from the street and driveway to the entrance and throughout the interior of the home.
- Have lightswitches controlled from within both house and garage.
- Use outdoor lighting equipment that is designed for outdoor use, with weatherproof cords, plugs, sockets, and connections.
- Be sure all lighting fixtures are properly shielded so there is no glare.
- Inspect all cords and plugs for signs of wear.
- Provide enough electrical outlets so that extension cords are not run across floors.
- If the electrical service is not adequate for your needs, have it upgraded.

REFERENCE ORGANIZATIONS

Agriculture Canada
Art Hazards Information Center, New York
Blue Cross Association, USA
Blue Cross of Canada
Canada Mortgage and Housing Corporation
Canada Safety Council
Canadian Agricultural Chemicals Association
Canadian Centre for Occupational Health and Safety
Canadian Coast Guard
Canadian Medic Alert Foundation
Canadian Standards Association
Consumer and Corporate Affairs Canada
Emergency Preparedness Canada
Fire Prevention Canada Association
Health and Welfare Canada
Industrial Accident Prevention Association, Ontario
Insurance Bureau of Canada
Labour Canada
Medic Alert, USA
Ministry of Health, Ontario
National Institute for Occupational Safety and Health
National Safety Council, USA
Office of the Dominion Fire Commissioner, Canada
Ontario Lung Association
Poison Control Centers
U.S. Consumer Product Safety Commission

ABOUT THE AUTHORS

Heward Grafftey received his Bachelor of Arts degree at Mount Allison University, majoring in Political Science and History, and his Bachelor of Civil Law degree at McGill University before being admitted to the Bar of the Province of Québec.

He was the Federal member of Parliament for the Québec riding of Brome-Missisquoi from 1958-68 and 1972-80. In 1962, Grafftey was named Parliamentary Secretary to the Minister of Finance, and was a delegate to the United Nations in 1958 and 1966. In 1979, he became the Minister of State for Social Programs and Minister for Science and Technology in the Clark administrative.

During his parliamentary career, Grafftey co-authored an all-party brief on motor vehicle and highway deaths and injuries, and appeared before the relevant U.S. Senate and House Committees, as well as before various state legislatures on the subject. He has been an advocate for the establishment of a National Accident Research Center in Canada and for government-sponsored research into the development of a prototype safety car. He has also played an active role in improving community emergency response systems. Grafftey has written many articles on the subject of accident prevention. He is also author of the books The Senseless Sacrifice: A Black Paper on Medicine, Lessons from the Past, a political work and Safety Sense on the Road.

He was named Queen's Counsel in 1981. He currently resides in Ottawa, where he has a practice in government relations with emphasis in the area of technology innovation. Mr. Grafftey is the Chairman of Safety Sense Enterprises, Inc.

Richard A. McInenly received his Ph.D from Michigan State University, majoring in Curriculum Development and Traffic Safety Education. He holds a Masters Degree from the same university in Curriculum Development and Instruction, as well as a Bachelor of Science degree from Utah State University.

McInenly previously spent twelve years with the Canada Safety Council in research and development. He has published numerous articles related to safety and co-edited the Canadian Dictionary of Safety Terms and co-authored Safety Sense on the Road.

McInenly offers consultant services through his firm, RAM Consulting-Educational. He is a member of the American Association for the Advancement of Automotive Medicine, Phi Delta Kappa, and the International Road Safety Committee of the World Safety Organization. McInenly is President of Safety Sense Enterprises, Inc.

NOTES